– A Half-Baked Life –

CLAUDE JENKS

– A Half-Baked Life –

My Story So Far

First published in 1991 in Great Britain
by Lime Tree
an imprint of the Octopus Publishing Group
Michelin House, 81 Fulham Road, London SW3 6RB

A CIP catalogue record for this book
is available from the British Library
ISBN 0 413 45251 4

Printed and bound in Great Britain
by Clays Ltd, St. Ives Plc

For Michael and Olga Toft

– *Foreword* –

by Brian Thompson

Last New Year's Eve I was entertaining about a hundred guests in my thirteenth-century manor house in Gloucestershire when my manservant called me away from a conversation in the library to say there was a stranger at the garden door who sought the courtesy of a bowl of water. He wished to test the inner tube of his bicycle for punctures. I went at once to see for myself.

Standing on the threshold with good-natured patience was a tall man wearing two balaclavas and with a piece of Christmas wrapping taped to one lens of his spectacles. He was white with driven snow. In one hand he held an inner tube and in the other a plastic bag, stuffed with paper.

That man was the author of the pages you are about to read. I ushered Mr Jenks to the kitchens. He told me he had come from Tewkesbury and was on his way to Chipping Sodbury. As he thawed I saw that he was a little older than myself and that life had perhaps treated him less kindly. I gave him a glass of cooking wine.

Shortly afterwards I was called away to see the New Year in and excused myself for a few moments. Returning to the kitchens at about two, I found my unexpected guest departed, leaving behind him, by some terrible oversight, the plastic carrier bag. It contained the manuscript of *A Half-Baked Life*.

I read a few pages, and then more. The noise of the party faded into a distant buzz as I read his work with something of the feelings ascribed to Salieri. At about five in the morning I was called away to referee a fierce argument between my wife and her acupuncturist. By then my mind was quite elsewhere – and has stayed there ever since.

I believe many readers of this amazing book will quickly experience the same haunting dislocation.

– One –

I begin, like Dante, in *media res*. Two men are rowing a bath-tub across the English Channel. They have been egged on by the *Daily Mail* and are being filmed by Movietone News, who are following in a steam launch. The seas are choppy and the bath-tub is taking water. Sitting at the tap end, blinded by smoke from the support craft, singing like Ophelia shortly before they came to take her away, is a thin, rabbity man in an oversize sou'wester. He wears an antic expression.

Someone from Movietone News calls to this man that unto him a son is born.

'Where?' he cries.

'In the circle of the Roxy cinema, Kimbolton.'

The man, the antic man, stands to offer a gap-toothed rendition of 'Rule Britannia', egged on by the *Daily Mail* and Movietone News. Like many an amateur before him, he waves his arms to conduct

an invisible orchestra. Cross seas and over-exuber-
ance do for him, and he pitches backwards into the
sea.

The year is 1932. The man is my father.

My mother had always wished for a girl and it was
her intention to call the child Lorraine. She was
disappointed in this as in so much else and I came
into the world Claude Lorraine Everitt Jenks, she
being an Everitt of Bromsgrove. As we have seen,
my father was not present at the birth. He came
home in disgrace, a laughing stock even to the
lunatic fringe among whom he had hitherto numbered his friends.

'There is no malice in the man,' Mother would
wail. 'There isn't a malicious bone in that man's
body. But his brain is on fire! I don't rightly know
what to call it in proper medical parlance. But for a
lay person, it is no joke.'

My father's disease was an incurable facetious-
ness. On trains and buses he would disgust passengers by smoking as many as five cigarettes at once.
He painted his ears green. He often wore the jacket
to his suit back to front and in this mode would
accost pretty girls and the more unworldly sort of
parson. It never occurred to him that these acts and
many others like them were making paupers of him
and his family.

'Bless this unhappy child!' my mother cried to

the old Queen Mary, holding me up over the heads of the crowd as Her Majesty was planting a tree in front of the Civic Hall, Leytonstone. 'For his Dad has as much brains as a bucket of slops.'

I was hardly ten months old, but can vividly remember the Queen narrow her eyes like Chester Conklin and look into my face with regal pity. A moment later my mother was hustled away, sobbing.

Poor woman. In Bromsgrove, the name of Everitt had some cachet among those who knew ironmongery: Grandpa Everitt's little shop in Talavera Street was a magnet to home improver and tradesman alike. But my father was banned from crossing the Bromsgrove Borough boundaries by Grandpa, upon pain of being nailed to the pavement. The sturdy world of ironmongery could have no dealings with a man who numbered his teeth. Talavera Street was not at home to someone who disrupted an Armistice Day parade in Yarmouth by appearing in a kirtle of kippers.

We lived like gypsies, except that what gypsies we met drove us away with sticks. My mother was forced to seek help from the Jenks side of the family. Her father-in-law, my paternal grandfather, lived in a tar-paper shack in rough woodland outside Bagshot. Tot though I was, I remember watching Grandpa Jenks respond to her pleas by seeming to personate a log of wood, a stone gatepost or a larch pole leaning against a barn.

'You're his Dad,' Mother implored. 'Can't you bring him down to earth? Say something. For the sake of this child here.'

Grandpa Jenks stood for what seemed like minutes, his head cocked to one side. We both knew that the old patriarch had not uttered since the Spanish Flu epidemic of 1919. We left him standing in the glade wherein his shack was set, his face a perfect *visage de bois*, a robin perched on his shoulder.

'Two barmpots from the same larder,' Mother shouted, as we ran through the woods for the bus to Bagshot.

Time for a coffee. The opening, over which I have had so many contrary and wayward thoughts, has resolved itself. Perhaps the chapters, as we gather pace, could be longer. I must think about this.

– *Two* –

Yesterday rain and gale force winds were forecast. My neighbour Mr Pocock carried in his deck loungers, his barbecue set and all the other paraphernalia of summer. After cleaning each item carefully, he stored them in the roof space of his garage. But today has dawned clear and mild with a golden autumnal stillness. As I write, I can see Pocock out on his lawn, staring at the milky blue sky with characteristic exasperation. He feels cheated. He feels – and I can see it in his stance, the very cut of his jib – horribly let down. Here, he seems to be saying to the gentle innocence of the day, here is a man whose prudence has been flung back into his face. What sort of reward is that?

After several very careful readings, I definitely feel the chapters should be longer. Easy enough to accomplish in my present mood. Gazing out on material existence this beautiful morning from my attic window I feel I have the understanding of the universe at my fingertips. Everything – the trees, the Pocock greenhouse reflecting back the sun in genial fashion, the stylish but needlessly provocative underwear of Mrs Pocock limp upon the line – all these conspire together to lend my enterprise strength, and confidence. And there was a very curious incident last night that lends my pen its racing swiftness.

Strictly speaking, the event took place this morning, in the still watches of the night, at about two. There was a sudden and massive crump as eight feet of bookshelves came away from the wall, bringing much of the plaster with them. I switched on the light to find confusion abounding. In the wreckage of planks and battens, woodscrews and (alas) Rawl-plugs there lay a hideous carnage. Reaumur's *Mémoires pour servir à l'histoire des insectes* stretched like an earthquake victim beside Tillotson on *The Great Western Railway Coach Works Depot*. Lytton Strachey was to be found beneath Kitchener of Khartoum, Ouida under Vita Sackville-West. Hawley's *Report on the Excavations at Stonehenge 1925–26* made an uneasy bedfellow with W. H. Uker's magisterial two-volume *All About Tea*. And much, much more besides.

I sat with one slipper in my hand, staring at the books and the ruined shelves and watching the white plaster dust billow towards me across the threadbare carpet. And, strange as it may seem, a huge welling joy spread through me. I seemed to be staring past these dear friends – my precious books, my most loyal companions – and gazing instead down long corridors of memory. So Proust felt when he dipped his madeleine in his tea – and heaven knows he was a man for a lengthy chapter, once he was up and running.

The faithful Underwood sat on my desk, next to a bottle of herbal pills for the relief of catarrh given to me by L. S. Lowry on a happy occasion. There was the ammonite from Ravenscar Bay in Yorkshire that dear old Van der Post and I had bickered over, all those years ago. There was my pebble in the shape of the Right Hon. Douglas Hurd, MP; some paperclips; a photograph of Mother, shading her eyes at a Co-op fête. And there, in front of all this, my heaped up books, a world upturned. I felt – I feel – a sign had been given to me. There was magic in the air. Even more to the good, I found a little book on Trembley I had lost these many years. I sat reading until dawn.

Grandpa Jenks it was who broke the deadlock of my childhood. He died. I discovered what my parents already knew, that he was possessed of a private income and had acted the goat in the way that he did purely out of spite. The money from the estate went to my father, who had now accepted, or so we thought, a responsibility previously sadly lacking in his affairs. But we reckoned without his congenital waywardness. He conceived, in perfect seriousness, the idea of teaching the Wehrmacht ballroom dancing. He set off shortly after for Berlin, armed with a wind-up gramophone and a selection of Victor Sylvester's Strict Tempo waltzes, foxtrots and quicksteps. Being a man of extraordinary extravagance in money matters – when he had any to hand – he decided to fly to Berlin, and we said goodbye to him at Heston Airport the night Chamberlain came back from Munich. As the famous piece of paper was being waved at one end of the field, my father was waving his brand new black fedora at the doorway to a Junkers 52/3m at the other. The silver trimotor taxied across the damp grass, almost unnoticed in the general hysteria, its tailplane emblazoned by a swastika on a red ground.

Apart from a whimsical and thoroughly indecent postcard saying that he had arrived safely and was lodging with a Frau Schacht, we heard no more from him, ever. His stated plan, to get set up in a nobby sort of premises and then send for us, came to nothing, defeated by world politics. Nor do I suppose the poor man prospered any better with Frau Schacht for companion. We may search history in vain for any leavening of the character of the German Army, either by means of ballroom dancing or general hilarity. My father was an instance of the truth that while the hour may indeed call forth the man, it also does the most grievous damage to others alive at the same time.

My portion of the inheritance was the tar-paper shack in the Bagshot woods, and there Mother and I repaired. Its glory – indeed, almost its only contents – was its library. The little hut was filled with, and in part constructed from, books. There were books piled to make tables and chairs, books as wardrobes, even an armchair fashioned from the weighty volumes of four quite separate encyclopedias.

'I'll teach you to read, Claudie,' my mother said. 'We shan't want for anything. We'll have a lot of fun, eh, you and me? Now you be a good boy while Mummy goes out to dig some roots for our tea.'

We lived very simply on rabbit stews and berries. So remote were we from the concerns of the twentieth century that we did not learn we were at war with the waltzing Wehrmacht of my father's fond dream until 1942, when some sort of Bagshot peasant passed by with a wheelbarrow of war scrap.

'That explains it, Claudie,' my mother remarked. 'Your Dad is ringed by the steel fortress of Jerry beastliness and serve him right. He always wanted to be different and now he's got his chance. Frau Schacht is welcome to him.'

The careful reader will have noticed that I have yet to speak in the story of my own life. This is not just a literary device. The plain fact is I did not utter until my tenth year, not for want of something to say, but out of embarrassed respect for my mother's position. She, poor woman, seemed not to notice, and spoke for both of us. I spent my days in reading and silent cogitation, in a way honouring the hearth gods of the place, for you will recall that Grandpa Jenks was also mum – in his case, for a generation.

Then, one day, this woodland idyll was shattered by the arrival of Mr Smight, the Schools Attendance Officer. He limped up the path, the hinges of a tin leg creaking, and explained to my mother she must fill in at least one government form if things were to be regularised between her and Mr Churchill.

'In fact,' he said, glancing round him at the shack, its environs, and the rabbit-skin shoes on Mother's feet, 'I should say you're good for half a dozen. But it is especially the Cee Aitch Eye Ell Dee that I've called about.'

Gerald Smight was then approaching sixty. My mother was barely thirty-five. It was love on the rebound, for Uncle Gerald – as my mother called him almost from his first visit – was as gloomy as my father had been hilarious. He had lost his leg in curtain fire at Arras and supposed as a consequence that no woman could truly love him. But from the moment my mother first clapped eyes on him, it was ardour. Soon, she was oiling his hinges and forbidding him teasingly from knocking out his pipe on the tin of his leg. And the years seemed to roll away from Uncle Gerald. He lost that habit of trying to swallow his own moustache and talking to his collar. He lost these habits, that is to say, with Mother. Towards me he was pink and hesitant. But one day the affair moved from flirtation to deep spiritual response in one go.

It happened like this. Uncle Gerald would sit watching me read, his brow furrowed, wondering, as he told me after, what colossal trauma had stolen away my powers of speech. One teatime – he usually called for tea at the end of a hectic day searching for truants – he smiled shyly at my mother and asked what I had been reading.

'I've been glancing at *Wace and Layamon, Two Arthurian Chronicles*, translated by Boyle in 1912,' I said.

I spoke without reflection and certainly had no idea of the consternation it would cause. Uncle Gerald's pipe fell from his lips, and my mother fainted clean away. Revived, she smothered my face with kisses and declared Uncle Gerald a power for good in the world, a waste in his present position of school bobby, and to be set alongside Helen Keller, etc. She asked me why I had never spoken before.

'I don't think I've ever before enjoyed a book as much,' I piped.

The two adults exchanged glances.

'And tell me then, Claude, what you find interesting in this dusty tome?' Smight asked, his hands trembling on his tobacco pouch.

'I have been quite interested in the Siege Perilous.'

'It's a blessed miracle,' my mother shouted. Uncle Gerald waved her to silence.

'And at what castle did that take place?'

'The Siege Perilous was a chair at the Round Table, Uncle Gerald, and not a military campaign.'

It was enough to satisfy them both that I was a normal healthy child, for up until then I truly believe my mother thought there was some case of demonic ventriloquism involved in my sudden acquisition of the power of speech. She asked me if I would be good enough to read to them both, and they sat with laced fingers listening to the fine old stories of Arthur and his court.

Was it accident, or had this moment created an opportunity for Smight that he seized in chivalrous fashion? At all events my mother henceforth treated him as Sir Galahad himself. We would wake at night to hear the faint creaking of his leg and find in the morning some small gift of his on the doorstep – perhaps some sugar in a little twist of paper, or a copy of *Picture Goer*. My mother took to washing her hair in the stream and singing wildly. So Igraine must have waited for Uther Pendragon.

And soon enough he began coming in the evening. My mother would sit with her head against his good leg, while he sat staring into the fire, not always thinking of love and that black day at Arras, but of Mrs Duxford, his mortal enemy, who had threatened to come and break his back for him if he pestered her any more about the Duxford twins, notorious absentees from school.

'I don't know how much longer I can keep quiet about His Nibs here, either,' he would say glumly to the bowl of his pipe. The servant of the law was aiding and abetting in breaking the law. His was a cruel dilemma.

One morning in January of 1943, I woke to find her gone. A note said that she was arranging about ration books, but there was something in the way the frost hung on the bough outside, some quality of the deep silence within the wood that told me my days of innocent scholarship were coming to an end. On Thursday of that week the Home Guard mounted an attack on me with blank cartridges and thunderflashes. It was all part of the war effort, but the shock of coming from a study of molluscs to the present time was severe. The Home Guard, bursting through the door and finding me engrossed in Thiele's *Handbuch der Weichterkunde*, arrested me on suspicion of spying and I was taken to the police station in Bagshot.

After some hours of confusion, a woman came into the room, wearing a maroon coat and a hat in the shape of a shoe. She introduced herself as Auntie

Elsie from Beckenham. I had never seen her before in my life.

'Are you perhaps Uncle Gerald's sister?' I asked cautiously.

'No,' the woman sobbed, falling to her knees and wiping the soot and cobwebs from my pullover with a little lace hanky. She was an Everitt, my mother's younger sister and a woman who felt disgrace most keenly.

'Has my mother got the ration books she went for?'

'Poor little beggar,' the kindly policeman muttered. Auntie Elsie tried to laugh gaily through her tears, without in the slightest deceiving me.

'No, my lamb, she hasn't. She and Uncle Gerald have gone to look for them in Scotland.'

'Where Uncle Gerald has a wife of his own,' the policeman added spitefully.

'And did they go by Flying Scotsman?'

'That's the size of it, sonny.'

'So while we're waiting, you can come and live with me in Beckenham,' Auntie Elsie cried hysterically.

'Which had a population of 50,429 in 1931,' I piped. I had been reading the armrest of Grandpa Jenks's unusual armchair. The policeman slapped the wall with the flat of his hand.

'What a ruddy war this is turning out to be,' he said in a choked voice.

Some papers were signed, I was given sixpence from the Poor Chest, and Auntie Elsie and I set off for Beckenham. The incomparable Jenks library, on which I had feasted my young mind, was left to moulder in the woods. After the war, I made some enquiries. With the astuteness I have noticed in many illiterates, the Duxford twins, the bane of Uncle Gerald's life, passed off the collection as their own to a bookshop in Oxford. And so profited from literature and scholarship in the only way open to them.

– *Three* –

Another short chapter in prospect. It can't be helped: the Pococks have heard the late night pounding of the Underwood through the party wall and appear to have mistaken it for some form of industrial undertaking. I am told today at the village post office that Pocock is bruiting it abroad that I am running a toy factory here. He has seen something similar on television. After close questioning of the post mistress, Mrs Heyhoe, I established that he had been watching a programme on Taiwan where whole families engage in outwork for the cheap toy market. It is quite characteristic of the Pococks that while they cannot possibly know what I am actually about, they have nevertheless sensed something which to them would be classified as untoward. Pocock has been standing on his lawn staring up at the attic window, a study in thwarted curiosity. From time to time he is joined by Mrs

Pocock. Their upturned faces convey a picture of generalised reprehension. It is still mild enough for them to be wearing shorts.

The Pococks have a perfect fervour for litigation. Thus when Mrs Duck, a lady of ninety, pinned a note to their wattle fence concerning a lost cat, the poor woman was immediately served with a letter from Pocock claiming malicious damage to his woodwork. Legal opinion was being sought. In this instance Mrs Duck's grandson Michael had somewhat to say. An amiable and often intoxicated plasterer, he found an opportunity to speak to the unspeakable Gordon Pocock in such terms that not only was he deterred from seeking justice under the law, but was moved to send Granny Duck a box of Cadbury's Roses and an invitation to view some holiday slides of a visit to Angoulême.

Thus it is that I sense some danger in my present enterprise. I am reinforced in this view by a conversation with another close neighbour, Ursula Wivens. She came round on some pretext and after only a few moments, asked directly to see the toy factory. How utterly ridiculous all this is. I explained that I was in fact writing a book, something I had hoped to keep from her, at any rate in the short term, for she is made of very combustible emotions when it comes to the arts. (She 'did' dance and drama at what she calls Coll' some time in, I imagine, the sixties.) I was saved from further explanation however by a grotesque accident.

For some weeks past – ever since the shelves collapsed, in fact – I have been trying to train the tortoise to sleep, or at any rate park, in a small cardboard box with the side cut out. This I have positioned in the kitchen, next to the fridge. Franco, for his part, will have none of it. His preferred hidey-hole is under the sofa in the living room. Well and good. Last night, Ursula was just telling me about her own new artistic venture – she is thinking of taking up stained glass in a small way – when the little scamp came out. I have to say that her general response to the unexpected in life may have contributed to the break-up of the marital arrangements she once had with Dr Stanley Wivens. For when Franco tried to climb over her shoe on the way to a dish of water, her reaction was what I can only describe as hysterical.

With a scream loud enough to bring Dr Wivens back from South Africa, where he is currently practising, she attempted to kick the tortoise through the open door. And though I picked him up and presented him to her formally, she screamed again and ran downstairs, her skirts held to her knees by shaking hands. Not a lover of the animal kingdom, therefore.

All this is certain to get back to the Pococks. It is all so demoralising. When Keats sat down to write 'Ode to a Nightingale' did he have any of this – he did not. He jumped up from his deckchair in Hampstead and went at it like a madman. La

Wivens, before she rent the air with her piercing screams, told me I could be the next Jack Higgins. I have no idea who Jack Higgins is, but I am sure he can't have had as many obstacles placed in his path as I. I have moved the desk to Mrs Duck's side of the house. She is as deaf as a post and sleeps on the ground floor; it is said in a hammock.

– *Four* –

Auntie Elsie lived in a small terrace house with, for some reason, a bust of Byron over the front door. The poet's nose had been broken off by enemy action, but he could be identified by his wide collar. Next door was Southey, beyond that Coleridge, and so on. Most hideous of all was Shelley, with half his head missing and a starling's nest on his good side. I am often accused of dwelling too much and too long on the war, but no one sent to queue for ten Passing Clouds and a handful of carrots and passing the ruined Shelley on the way could easily forget the moment, nor the era in which it took place.

Auntie Elsie's husband was Uncle Dick, away at the front: to be specific, in Oswestry, as an unpaid lance-corporal of the Royal Army Pay Corps. My aunt's house, Byron notwithstanding, was hardly a place of books or learning. It was neat as a pin, smelled faintly of Blue Poppy scent and in the evenings (more often than not) resounded to the melancholy broodings of the Ink Spots, a special favourite of Aunt's. She would heat the curling tongs on the gas stove and with half-closed eyes sing the unanswered and perhaps unanswerable question *Why do you whisper, green grass?* To my much more obvious questions, viz, *Is there any news of my mother and Uncle Gerald?* Auntie Elsie would simply burst into tears.

In fact, though it slows down the narrative, I should perhaps say in a brief aside what *had* happened to my truant mother and her limping inamorata. They had indeed fled to Arbroath, in order to confront Mrs Gerald Smight with the hapless circumstance of having fallen in love. Annie Smight was a native Scot with a practical bent. The lovers arrived just as she was in the process of opening a fish and chip shop. There was much to forgive, but the good-hearted Caledonian forgave, and the three of them began a curious ménage à trois, some aspects of which bear upon my story at a later date. For the moment, I must ask the reader to ponder instead the situation as it obtained in De Quincey Street, Beckenham.

One day in the late spring of 1944 I was on my way to a haircut. Those of you who know Beckenham well will recall that behind MacFisheries, on the other side of the road to Walpole and Beckwith's, was a barber's, housed in a narrow wooden hut. It was approached up an alley filled with the mysterious flotsam of urban life – odd socks, milk crates, past copies of the *Daily Mirror*, spokeless bicycle wheels and the like. I picked my way to the front door and upon entering, found a chair empty. In fact the whole shop was deserted. I duly sat down and studied the dusty bottles of bay rum and pomade while waiting for service. There was a curtained partition at the back of the premises where I knew the staff – that is to say Sid Walters and his assistant Snowy – were wont to make a cup of tea. The curtains parted – and I was struck dumb with amazement: for the man who was whisking the towel about my neck was none other than General Sir Bernard Montgomery, later Lord Montgomery of Alamein!

You can imagine the thoughts and emotions that flooded through me. Monty extinguished a rare hand-rolled cigarette and picked up the scissors with snapping fingers. There was absolutely no mistaking that narrow skull, those piercing blue eyes and a moustache trimmed to perfection. I was in a turmoil of schoolboy excitement. This was the first famous person I had ever met. At the same time, the very fact that Monty was masquerading as a barber in Sid Walters' place put me on the *qui vive*, as they say in France. Catching his eye, I bowed my head.

'Sit still, sonny,' the hero of the Western Desert commanded in the clipped tones for which he was famous. 'This is cold steel I have in my hand here, not a banana. I could biff an ox with these scissors.'

He snipped expertly, while whistling 'Tipperary' a little off-key. My mind raced. Here was the greatest field commander of the Second World War administering a short back and sides to a Beckenham schoolboy! What could it mean? There was in fact only one explanation.

'You are, I take it, incognito, sir,' I whispered.

'I'm what, sweetheart?' Monty rapped out, with a dry laugh.

'Your secret is safe with me.'

The effect of this remark was very dramatic. He paused, the scissor points nestling against my jugular.

'What secret? Who's been talking? What have you heard, you little pimple?'

'I am Claude Jenks,' I said. 'The boy who captured the spy in Bassenthwaite's.'

Monty stared at my reflection in the fly-blown mirror.

'So it was you, was it?'

Earlier in the year I had been in Bassenthwaite's the chemist's on some errand for Auntie when my attention was drawn to the back of a large man acting under suspicious circumstances. The awkwardness of his demeanour, the general cut of his jib convinced me I had a fifth columnist at my disposal. Plucking a hairbrush from a cabinet I thrust the wooden handle deep into the man's back

with a hearty cry of *'Hands Hoch! Alles Kaput!'* –
only to discover that the man in question was not a
German spy but the Reverend Sidebotham from St
Mary's and All the Bells. The shock proved too
great for the portly clergyman and he fell forward
into a display of walking sticks, having suffered a
sudden but on my part unintentionally caused heart
attack. The story was quite well known in the
Beckenham area.

'So you're the one that did for the old Rev, are
you?' Monty mused. 'And look at him now – a
vegetable at his own Harvest Festival.'

'I thought he was a German paratrooper,' I explained.

'Oh yes,' Monty scoffed. 'Who had just popped
in for a tube of pile ointment before heading off to
have a go at old Winnie, I don't think. That man
had the nicest head of hair for miles round, clergy
or no. You put the fear of God up him and – bingo!
– he's gone stark white!'

He snipped furiously at my own scalp. I could
tell his mind was seething almost as badly as my
own.

'What's all this about secrets?' he said at length.
'I don't like people minding my own business for
me. Is it about the petrol – is that what you're on
about? That petrol was come by legally and there's
no one can say different, I don't care who they are.'

'I was thinking more of the Second Front.'

'The second what?' Monty asked with poised blades.

'The invasion of Europe.'

His eyes narrowed.

'Invasion?'

'The Allied invasion.'

'What about it?'

'That's why you're here in Beckenham. For some purpose, for some secret reason to do with counter-intelligence perhaps.'

He studied me yet again in the mirror.

'Maybe I am, and maybe I'm not.'

'I understand.'

Monty wiped some sweat from his brow with the cuff of his white coat. He puffed at my neck with a bulb filled with powder and whipped away the cloth. A thought occurred to me.

'Maybe you're here to meet with General Eisenhower,' I suggested.

'Schtum!' Monty commanded, a finger to his lips. 'Walls have ears, eh? Careless talk costs lives.'

'Schtum it is, sir.'

He ruffled the hair he had just combed.

'Be a good kid and buzz off now, and not a word to no one, about the invasion, the petrol or nothing.'

'Say nothing about the petrol,' I repeated loyally.

'Specially about the petrol. Now buzz off. I got some phone calls to make,' Monty muttered, opening the till and pressing a sixpence into my hands. He refused to give me his autograph and retired behind the curtain, presumably to speak with his Chiefs of Staff over scrambler telephone. I ran home, eager to tell Auntie that the Second Front was imminent. I would not say how or why I knew this, but the news of it would interest her, for she often asked me whether I thought Uncle Dick would be posted abroad.

She met me coming out of the sitting room, adjusting the hem to a floral print blouse of a style I notice is now somewhat back in fashion. She seemed flustered.

'Great news, Auntie! Crumbs, have we got company? It's not Uncle Dick, is it?'

I pushed past her to enter the warm and cosy room – and the whole world reeled! There, in front of the gas fire, standing on our rag-felt carpet and fiddling hastily with the cotton belt to his slacks was the Supreme Allied Commander, General Dwight D. Eisenhower! To be sure he was dressed in the uniform of a top sergeant but of course I recognised him instantly. He smiled a little sheepishly.

'Hiya, kid, howya doin'?' Eisenhower enquired.

'Very well, General,' I managed to croak.

'This is my sister's little boy, the one I was telling you about,' Auntie Elsie shrilled from the doorway.

'You don't have to call me General, son,' Eisenhower murmured.

'Can I call you Ike?'

He looked at Auntie, who was laughing hysterically and tearing at the hair round her ears.

'Didn't I tell you what a card he is?' she shrieked.

'Look, sir, I have just come from Monty.'

'Monty?'

'General Montgomery. He's waiting for you at Sid Walters'. It's a barber's shop behind MacFisheries.'

'MacFisheries,' Ike repeated slowly.

I have read subsequently about Eisenhower's slow and methodical habits of speech. He displayed them to the full that afternoon.

'You met Monty behind MacFisheries.'

'And now *you*! This is fantastic! Does Uncle Dick know about your visit here? I bet he does! I bet he'd give anything to be here now.'

Ike and Auntie Elsie went back out into the hall. Through the door I could hear raised voices. By now Auntie was screeching with uncontrollable laughter and I could hear Ike say, more than once, 'Ah, come on now, Elsie, cut it out.' To which she shouted, 'I can't help it, I think I'm going out of my mind.' At last Ike came back into the room. He rummaged in his pockets and fished out a florin.

'Here, take this, kid. I want you to have it. You're a damn smart kid. You guessed the truth. I don't know how you did it, but you did. I'm here to see your man Monty.'

'About the Second Front.'

'You got it. The Second Front.' Ike ran his tongue over his teeth and studied his hands, which were still shaking a little. 'It's all fixed, the whole show's ready to roll. But I gotta get back to London to talk with your Premmy-Ear.'

'Mr Churchill,' I supplied.

'That's the guy. So until I see Mr Churchill – '

' – even *after* you've seen Mr Churchill – ' Auntie shouted from the hall.

' – Yeah, even *after* I've seen Mr Churchill, I'm going to have to swear you to an oath of secrecy. You know what an oath is?'

'Oh yes,' I piped.

'And you'll say nothing?'

'Never?'

'Never.'

'Even to Uncle Dick?'

'Especially to Uncle Dick,' Auntie bellowed.

'Elsie, will you let me handle this?'

'Could I have your autograph, General?'

'Eisenhower don't give no autographs,' he said. He shared with Monty a certain laxity in matters of grammar. But he too ruffled my already ruffled hair.

'If I hurry, I can catch Monty,' he said.

'The shop shuts at six.'

'Uhuh. Gotcha. Behind the MacFisheries, uh?'

'Opposite Walpole and Beckwith's. Though I expect you know that.'

'Okay kid,' he said. 'Gotta go now. Must keeping moving. Can't stand still. Not a word to anyone now, you hear?'

In leaving, he squeezed Auntie's waist. She gave him back several tins.

'Don't be a jerk, Elsie. Take the damn rations.'

'I can't, I can't,' she wept.

So it was that we dined that night off a piece of snoek and a tomato each. Auntie Elsie was quite beside herself and took to straightening up the larder. I munched on my snoek, thrilled with the events of the day.

'General Eisenhower's a very nice man, isn't he, Auntie Elsie?'

'Yes,' she cried wildly. 'Just look how many Kilna jars we've got, Claude. Quite a collection.'

'And Monty's nice. He's a whizz at cutting hair, too, don't you think?'

'You look very smart.'

'It's been a very exciting day, Auntie. I don't suppose anything else could happen half as exciting.'

But I was wrong. About nine in the evening, there was a commotion at the front door. Auntie and I jumped up. Into the sitting room came a kitbag, followed by the perspiring Uncle Dick. His spectacles were taped together, there was a red pimple on the side of his nose and he smelt of trains and soot. He had left Oswestry that morning at seven, and travelled to London via Leeds and Hull. Auntie fell on the floor in a dead faint at the sight of him.

We shared a cup of cocoa while Uncle Dick

revived her spirits, by telling some amusing anec-
dotes of the war in Oswestry, as when for example
the imprest account of the Sutherland Highlanders
had been sixpence short, only for the coin to be
discovered in the turn-ups of Band Major Rutter;
and other yarns of the service.

'And how have you been, old Claude?'

'He's been a bit off colour,' Auntie Elsie shouted.
'In fact, I may keep him off school for a day or so.'

'Off colour?'

'General Eisenhower gave me some money today,'
I blurted out.

'He's sickening for something!'

'General Eisenhower? Where was this?'

'Here, Uncle Dick. I wasn't supposed to tell you,
but – ' Auntie Elsie fainted again, this time dragging
the blackout curtains to the floor with her.

That night, while I lay in bed and thought about
the Second Front, there was a gentle knock at the
door, and Uncle Dick came in. He sat on the end of
the bed for some time, giving an occasional twang
to his issue braces, as if deep in thought.

'War's a funny business, Claude old chum,' he
muttered. 'And your Auntie's a fine well-set-up
young woman.'

'Pogh! but she's just a woman, Uncle Dick.'

'She may have the measure of *me* all the same.'

'But you know more about the monastic history
of Beckenham than any man living.'

'Much good has it done me,' he said bitterly.

'Your glads and dahlias won prizes before the war.'

'Auntie's told me about Monty. You're sure it wasn't Sid's brother from Walworth?'

'Crumbs, Uncle Dick. Of course it wasn't.'

'No,' he said doubtfully.

Before extinguishing my night light, he gave me threepence.

'Night night, Claude.'

'Don't let the fleas bite, Uncle Dick.'

He turned at the door.

'And General Eisenhower was definitely here, was he?'

'Oh, definitely.'

In the morning, he was gone. Six days later, the invasion of Europe commenced. The military police came round to the house to remind Uncle that he was expected to take part, but after looking under the beds and so forth, left. Auntie and I wrote to the Army address in Oswestry, saying I had made the whole thing up. She said I had done a very silly thing by revealing the whereabouts of the Supreme Allied Commander; and on reflection, I agreed. When I was a little older, I wrote to Ike, who was by now President of the United States. After some months, I got back a signed photograph of him sitting at the desk in the Oval Office. I have it by me as I write.

– *Five* –

There has been an almighty altercation at the Grove
Road Evening Centre. It appears that Mr Pocock,
under the guise of attending 'The Wines of France,
an Introduction', has actually enrolled for
'Advanced Figure Drawing and Painting'. This
seemingly innocent switch of interests was discovered by Mrs Pocock, who drove down to the
Centre last night in the second car to remind her
husband he had promised to ask the class back for
a tasting of the ten-litre drum of *vin de table* they
had picked up for a song in Nantes. Finding him
absent from the class – indeed, discovering his name
did not appear on the register – she scoured the
building. The shame-faced Pocock was hauled out
of the attics while engrossed in an excited charcoal
study. The model was none other than Mandy Bott,
of Wilks' Garage, all eleven stone of her in Renoir-
esque pose.

Pocock's stab at the vocabulary of line and form was by all accounts tending towards the lubricious. This may have been an accidental effect of where he was placed in the packed circle of art lovers that surrounded young Miss Bott – that is to say, at the front and quite close to. No matter that he shared the class with men of the stamp of Lionel Chew, a Life Inspector of the Prudential Assurance Co., an erstwhile friend of the Pococks and fellow caravanner. Mrs P. burst in upon what she perceived as untowardness on a grand scale. Harsh words were spoken. There were certain remarks addressed to Mr Chew that no gentleman could suffer. Mandy Bott so far forgot herself as to call Pocock's wife a jealous old bag. The class ended in uproar.

As I say, all this took place last night and I have pieced it together from a fairly phosphorescent exchange between the Pococks under the roof of their newly re-creosoted carport when they returned home. Marion Pocock had some wild words to say about adult education: it ended by her pouring away the many litres of *vin de table* down the road drain.

'My godfathers, Marion, have you gone mad?' I heard Pocock cry in anguish.

Thinking about it in the light of a new day, albeit an inclement one, with strong westerly winds and squally showers, has led me gently on to recall a most curious occasion on which Alfred Brendel and I once found ourselves sharing the same amenities at Bristol Temple Meads. The connection is loosely that of education, yet with interesting meteorological undertones.

Brendel and I were waiting for the London train. Though it has strictly no bearing on the story, some might find interest in the cause of the delay, which was a rain of small red North African frogs at Newport. These creatures had been sucked up by some especially stiff winds blowing off the Sahara and carried *nolens volens* across huge tracts of land and water; to be deposited, as I say, on the upline platform of the respected and venerable town in Gwent. I confess I should like to have seen it. For ten minutes, to the consternation of the chapel-loving Gwentians, it rained red frogs from a clear sky.

The driver of the train, a Methodist, very creditably refused to move until the frogs had been collected up in buckets (as many as showed signs of life) and taken to an Animal Sanctuary. This simple act of mercy triggered an ugly situation. There proved to be a shortage of buckets at Newport BR and soon an irate and self-styled market analyst of youthful years began kicking the frogs that lay ankle deep on the platform onto the line. This was of course the very reverse of Driver Watkins' intention. An altercation arose, not less impassioned than the one embroiling Mr Pocock and the life class at the Grove Road Centre last night. A Mr Herbert Ingram, pensioner and veteran of Arnhem, jumped down on to the line and started to throw back the frogs that the young market analyst had kicked there. The delayed passengers quickly took sides. There ensued a general fracas.

Driver Watkins was dragged from the cab of his engine and sought refuge in the Flag and Shovel store on Platform 3. It was this more than anything else that muddied the organisational waters, for now a relief driver had to be sent by taxi from Cardiff. Meanwhile, although many of the frogs had been shooed into the station carpark, those of Mr Ingram's persuasion in the matter had climbed down on to the permanent way and were blocking the tracks. Assistant Station Master Probert suffered a mild stroke, etc. etc. The problems escalated with every passing second.

Brendel and I had no inkling of this, however, in the damp quiet of the male conveniences at Temple Meads. I had of course recognised the pianistic genius immediately from the little strips of Elastoplast he wore on his fingers – that are to many his trademark. There was in fact a third person present who embarrassed us both by addressing Brendel in a loud and accusatory voice.

'You're Roy Hudd, aren't you?' this man said.

'I'm afraid not.'

'Don't give me that,' the man scoffed. 'Anyway, if you're not Roy Hudd, I bet you wish you were.'

I had seldom heard anything so preposterous.

'This gentleman is not Roy Hudd, nor I imagine

does he have any wish to be Roy Hudd,' I felt obliged to say with spirit.

'And who are you, four-eyes?' the stranger retorted, pushing his face close to mine. He was one of those who are prone to calling their adversaries 'pal', a class of psychopath I have met with more than once in recent years.

'You will see that I am offering no resistance to you whatsoever,' I said, suspended by my shirt front but retaining dignity and rationality. The stranger released his grip on me and I fell to the floor.

'Don't forget,' the oaf now said to Brendel, with stabbing motions of his finger, 'it's people like me what pay your wages. We put you up there in the first place. I'm disgusted.'

He tucked in his shirt and, with a last glower round, tramped up the steps. The concert pianist and I were alone. I felt the situation deserved retrieving. When we came over to the washbasins, I fancy I startled and perhaps flattered the great musician a little by enquiring boldly and directly who first taught him the piano.

Surprise and even alarm passed across his face. He owned somewhat haltingly that he had been taught by a Miss Ivy Comstock, who lived next to the Co-op on Mill Lane, in Pontefract. This was news indeed.

'And how old were you at the time?' I enquired, quite expecting him to say that the worthy Miss

Comstock had lifted him from his cot to introduce his tiny fingers to the scale of C. The great concert pianist's reply was thus doubly unexpected.

'Eleven,' he said. 'Well, eleven going on twelve.'

This in a faintly challenging tone of voice, Brendel eyeing me up and down the while. Here was a little detail of his career I had not previously known about; something not to be found on even the most extensive sleeve notes to his wide-ranging repertoire of gramophone recordings. Before I could enquire further, the distinguished Austrian explained that he had his bike with him and was anxious lest it be stolen before the arrival of the express.

'But there is so much I would like to discuss with you. Your wonderfully sure touch, for example.'

'Another time, perhaps.'

'You won't join me in a cup of tea at the buffet?'

Brendel backed hastily away.

'Look,' he said. 'I'm just not like that, okay? I've nothing against those that are, but you definitely picked the wrong bloke.'

He ran lightly up the stairs, and I was left to ponder instead the character of the mysterious Miss Comstock, pianoforte teacher of Pontefract. We can surely say of her that history has ignored a small heroine of instrumental tuition. Indeed, I wonder whether a subscription fund for a plaque or some other form of memorial to this remarkable lady might one day find merit. I can easily envisage her, stern but possessed of an inner fire, her head decorated by coiled plaits in the style known as earphones, her piano stool bulging with Schubert. How Brendel came to be in Pontefract is something I have not yet been able to establish.

The London train came at last – not without a generous spattering of frogs – and the last I saw of Brendel was a forlorn figure as we drew out from Platform 4. The maestro's bicycle had been refused on to the train by the senior conductor, P. P. Anantramiah. This man is of Madrasi extraction and I should add utterly remorseless in his application of British Rail bye-laws.

'But you have seriously inconvenienced one of the most luminous music talents of our times,' I protested.

'Yes, yes,' Anantramiah shouted. 'And this what you are giving me is not saver ticket, not supersaver ticket, nor it is standard fare ticket. This is ticket Admit One to Conway Castle.'

There was little of music at Clagg Lane Secondary Modern, Beckenham, to resume my own history. The headmaster was the infamous Mad Jack Morris, possessed of a steel hook in place of his right hand, which had been blown off in a fume cupboard accident some thirty years earlier. I can see him now, collecting up examination papers by spiking them as deftly as any park keeper. Chemistry was a subject no longer taught at the school and in place of the physical sciences we were taught cookery by the Amazonian Miss Phibbs, a lady of quite remarkable *embonpoint*. Since the materials for her steak and kidney pie were not to be got in wartime, nor indeed had ever been seen by her pupils, the lessons were almost entirely theoretical. The good woman made some effort to inject a note of realism by passing out little squares of brown wrapping paper and the like: but it was hardly enough. It seemed a humorous thing to many of my colleagues to eat the paper with much lip-smacking and cries of 'Yum Yum' and the like.

I have often been asked why it was I did not attend a grammar school, where surely my steps would have been directed to higher education, possibly Oxford or Cambridge, and thereafter a very different life. The answer lies with the curious circumstances of my childhood – the tar-paper shack in the woods, a mother's fondness, the eclecticism of my early reading and so on. Strange to relate, these things held me back in the race for academic excellence, in so far as Beckenham had organised such an event. I was certainly treated by Mad Jack Morris as some kind of freak. He never tired of saying so.

Those who have read in idleness the expression 'his eyebrows knitted together' and passed it over, taking the metaphor to be mere poetic licence, can never have met Morris when he was under the press of strong emotion. He was possessed of eyebrows hardly smaller than bicycle mudguards and they knitted, wove and intermingled most horribly.

'I do not need telling by some snot-nosed brat that Crippen's Christian names were Hawley Harvey,' he thundered on one characteristic occasion. 'Nor do I need to know at my time of life, certainly not in the context of the work I have before me, that Sir Walter Scott is buried at Dryburgh. Nor that – ' scrabbling with his good hand he sought a place in my essay ' – nor that Jan Van Ruysbroek's major inspiration for a life of mysticism was the *De Origine Monasterii* of Henry Pomerius.'

Especially incensed by this last he struck himself a savage blow between the eyes with his hook. White froth flecked his lips.

'I have no need of these facts. These facts serve no purpose but to irritate and disgust me. Such erudition is a form of dumb insolence – don't interrupt when I'm talking! Your assignment was to write a simple essay on "A Day in the Life of a Penny". This is a school, not some hothouse of literary pansies, some *congerie* of saloon bar philosophers and their tarts.'

'Mr Banarjee said – '

He held up his hook in fearsome warning.

'Mr Banarjee is an Emergency Trained Teacher,' he whispered. 'You do as that poor helpless old man asks, or it's the strap. You freak! You gangling bundle of molecules! You know what a penny is, don't you?'

'I suppose Mr Banarjee intends the copper penny, first introduced in 1797, sir, but later . . .'

'He means,' Mad Jack said dangerously, 'the penny.'

There were many examples of this sort of thing throughout my school career. Almost every day boys were taken away by the police, never to return. In time the luckless Banarjee joined them, after an unfortunate late night incident on the Southern Railway. The staffroom was perpetually riven by faction. Morris rampaged up and down the school sowing discord wherever he went. His special target among the boys was, as I have said, myself – Jenks. He reserved even greater venom for a member of his own profession, the diminutive Dr Mostyn.

The good Mostyn taught mathematics and religious instruction, doubling up with games and PE. His was a generous portfolio and though a little shaky in some respects – I fancy I once floored him on the cosmogony of the Scandanavian myths – he was a decent enough human being. His fault was in claiming to have played Rugby for Llanelli and London Welsh. This drove Mad Jack Morris into paroxysms of anger. The Headmaster spent an inordinate amount of time trying to disprove Dr Mostyn's sporting career. He pored over the relevant club records, wrote to distinguished pre-war internationals and pestered the life out of the sports desk of the *Daily Express*. His mania was simply explained: it was his own proud boast that he had once been offered a trial by Arsenal. Dr Mostyn was stealing his athletic thunder.

'You show me, Jenks,' he would rave, his steel hook caught in my nostril, 'you show me a dwarf that plays rugby – apart from standing in for the ball on occasion – and I'll show you a woman goalie in the First Division.'

Women figured large in his conversation. He seemed both entranced and repelled by them.

'And there was that clown Napoleon,' he would rant, during class discussion of the Battle of Waterloo, 'standing there with his hand inside his waistcoat, fondling himself like any woman! Your typical Frenchman, standing there like a great girl's blouse, while the Royal Scots Greys thundered towards him!'

On the death of General Gordon he was even more acid.

'Done to death by a bunch of girlie-wirlie fuzzy-wuzzies with their hair done up in plaits, mincing up the steps to the Governor's Residence like tarts on Derby Day.'

'Old Gordon ought to have seen them off, like,' suggested Fladge, a huge boy who, though only thirteen, already sported a full moustache. Fladge was slow on the uptake, to be sure, the way house-bricks are, or wheelbarrows, but here was a crux in history he could understand.

'Yes, Fladge! Seen them off, sent them scampering in their nighties. Good lad, you've caught my drift exactly!'

Then, one glorious and never-to-be-forgotten day, the unthinkable came to pass: Mad Jack Morris was himself taken away in a police van. We boys celebrated each in our different ways. Fladge and some of his cronies set fire to the school, pelting the fire brigade when they arrived with bricks and soot bombs. Some chaired Dr Mostyn about the playground and some, I am sorry to say, cornered Miss Phibbs. For myself I had but one ambition and that was to remove myself from the records of the Beckenham Education Authority for ever. Let us put it this way, that while I did not materially assist the conflagration now licking at the doors of the school office, I did nothing to prevent it either. I saw with a poet's clarity of vision as the flames danced their fandango on the hated portals, that my career as a schoolboy would – within a very few minutes – be so much ash. And if Fladge could grow a moustache, why not I? I was already a tall lad, though inclined to the gangly. My way to freedom lay in the adult world. I decided to grow a moustache.

Auntie Elsie received this news in characteristic fashion – she burst into uncontrollable tears.

'You don't just grow a moustache,' she wept, missing the point entirely. 'I just wish that fool

Dick was here, he'd tell you about that sort of thing.'

But that, so to speak, was the extent of the shot in her locker. She knew as well as I that Uncle Dick was doing two years in the glasshouse for desertion.

'I feel I am ready for the wider world, Auntie Elsie.'

'But what about your pump bag with your initials on it? What about your swimming costume and your footie boots? All your little friends?'

The good woman had little or no concept of school life. I compromised by staying for the VE night party, when De Quincey Street revealed a dionysiac side to itself I had not previously suspected. A small victory bonfire soon escalated into a Roman bacchanalia, in which I have to say Auntie Elsie took full part, dressed in green satin shorts and tap shoes. Grown men ran about giggling and hitherto respectable ladies of the cut of Mrs Huxtable and others sang indecent songs about the Axis leaders. Flags were flown from every bedroom window – not all of them Union Jacks. Indeed I noted Brazil, Iceland and Turkey among the more bizarre expressions of patriotism.

'Claudie wants to grow a moustache,' Auntie felt emboldened to shout from time to time, bringing a hail of raucous ribaldry down on my head. As the night wore on, the mood turned maudlin. Bluebirds were promised next day over the white cliffs of

Dover. Sobbing recollections were made of the night the nightingale sang in Berkeley Square.

'Now what's all this about a 'tash, Claude my son?' a sozzled old fool enquired. 'Got sumfink you want to tell me?'

'Only that your fly is undone, Mr Ridley.'

Bootless to explain further: next morning I took a train to London and presented myself at the first public library I came across. Taking down the nearest volumes to hand, I began a haphazard but joyous study of metamorphic rocks. I can't say I understood all that I read and I have by now forgotten even the crudest outline of the subject. But the sense of having been freed from prison was exhilarating, as I explained to J. B. Priestley when we rose from our desks at closing time. I had noticed the novelist, playwright and broadcaster reading intently from *Gray's Anatomy*. I do not claim to have had a deep or in any way intellectual conversation with the bluff Bradfordian. We merely exchanged a few hearty sentiments on the pavement outside. Moustache or not, Priestley took me for what I was, in my own heart – a young man with ambition.

'And a bloody lanky one into the bargain, lad.'

So ended the Beckenham phase of my life.

– *Six* –

I have been taken to task by Mrs Strutt, to whom I gave sight of some earlier pages, for failing to make clear that I am her lodger and that the domestic circumstances I have so far touched on have omitted this fact. This has irked her; and Strutt in pique, though a common event, is a jangling thing to behold. What little civilities we have been able to maintain are for the time being withdrawn. More ludicrously, she would like a number of things included in the manuscript, viz. That she has a barometer that has been in her family for four generations; and that she once played the cello for the Duke of Windsor. Remonstrance has been in vain. Literary objections have been swept aside. When I tried to explain the craft of writing as simply as I could to someone who must make several drafts of a note to the milkman, the good woman exploded.

'You put the Pococks into your story easily

enough, oh yes, but not old Struttie. And while we're on the subject, we'll have no more visits from that Wivens woman. I saw that, I'm not blind. I keep a respectable house here, or it was until you turned up.'

Briefly, then, Mrs Strutt is a raddled and hennaed hag with a penchant for chiffon scarfs who is in possession of a mahogany and gilt barometer presented to her grandfather, the Cruiserweight Champion of the Home Fleet for 1909. Its provenance is attested to by a small brass plaque. In any practical sense, it is useless, since both indicators have fallen from their pivot and are resting at the bottom of the glass. It is a common topic of conversation with the hideous Strutt that she must one day get that old barometer looked at by experts. As to the other matter, the cello recital she would have me refer to – this was an alfresco performance of 'The Grand Old Duke of York' at Brownie camp. The venue was Felixstowe and we are asked to believe the event to have been of world-shattering importance.

'Which it was! There was all shades of Brownie running around Felixstowe that year. They was jabbering in a dozen different tongues. There was some that only ate rice.'

Thus Strutt on internationalism. I have not checked the annals of Felixstowe to establish whether or not it ever played host to Brownies from many lands. Suppose Mrs Strutt to be telling the truth: this would at least, or in part, explain the royal presence. It stretches the imagination to suppose that the royal visitor to Felixstowe overheard the young Strutt by accident, while, for example, walking to the corner shop for his morning paper; or, in climbing a fence, came upon the elfin figure in the woods. More likely it was an official presence – that is to say, he drove past a line of performing Brownies in (I hope for his sake) a closed car. We must presume, incidentally, the Duke of Windsor was then Prince of Wales: in Mrs Strutt's rendering of the story he is always simply David. There is an ancient snapshot of her at this same camp, looking as belligerent as she does now and holding not a cello, but a dixie and ladle. The reader must come to his own judgement on the matter.

But all this is beside the point. I must bring you at once to an anecdote of my earlier years throwing more strange light on our troubled but remarkable century.

Gandhi as I knew him was polite, courteous and possessed of an inner strength that far exceeded the ordinary resilience and – how shall we say – fatalism of the dedicated home weaver. I have a very clear picture of him, dressed in white, his spectacles fogged, his furled umbrella signalling furiously to the thunder of an oncoming tram. We were not in Bombay. To the very contrary. Oranges and lemons went the bells of St Clement's as the founder of modern India and I wrestled with his shoe, jammed in the junction points that in those days bestrewed Ludgate Circus. The year was 1946.

The immediate post-war years were a very tight corner for a boy, no matter how tall and gangly. Peace came with some modicum of watery sunshine, but was all too soon characterised by fog, rain and general inclemency. The lights that came up in London, so yearned for in popular song, fell some way short of Babylonian excess. I groped about from one yellow island to another, experiencing darkness at noon, my shanks wrapped in newspaper against the cold. Austerity marched with me. I very quickly discovered that it was not so easy to grow a moustache as I had envisioned. For a while, in order to compete in the job market, I was forced to go about with a burnt-cork substitute on my upper lip.

Life was hard and my lack of years was making it harder. What I needed most were long trousers.

I can remember in particular applying for a post with the old Great Western Railway, and competing with two former sergeant majors, a rear-gunner and a chief petty officer of the WRENS. They amused themselves by trying to post me through a grilled window in the candidates' waiting room. I was accordingly interviewed hanging upside down out of the open window – and with a dizzying view of the approach to the main line platforms below. Yet

I will say this for the old GWR. It was a stickler for fair play.

'Have – you – any – prior – experience – of – carriage-washing?' the clerk bellowed slowly and patiently as the mighty expresses ran into Paddington fifty feet below.

'None.'

'Next question. A – man – has – five – sheep. Each – sheep – has – four – lambs. Two – sheep – and – three – lambs – fall – over – the – cliff. How – many – sheep – and – lambs – are – left?'

'Where was this?' I temporised, my face blackened with soot, my eyes as swimmy as infected oysters.

After many similiar false starts, though not all of them as dangerous to life and limb, I found a position with Mr Oliphant, who had a little business cleaning and reblocking trilby hats. This was located at Liverpool Street, and served the men of affairs who streamed through there daily, intent upon post-war reconstruction. The work was clean and safe, and my employer something of a philosopher.

'Look at this lot,' Oliphant would observe glumly of our potential customers as they marched up the concourse. 'Tat for titfers. Were it not for the Bishop of Ely and men of his ilk, Jenks, my respect for the present-day would be as nothing. These are strange times.'

'But we won the war, Mr Oliphant.'

'After a fashion. In a manner of speaking. We

have won the war, only to cram some shapeless felt on our heads in place of what ought to have been the victor's laurels. There's no snap to our brim, if you get my meaning.'

He was a man who knew trilbies. How many times have I seen him bring an unfortunate's hat into our narrow work-room and transform it from something fit only for scarecrows to a hatter's work of art. There were photographs on the wall of Mr Oliphant seen shaking hands with the likes of George Raft and Michael Wilding. There was a framed letter from the Crazy Gang. Whistling tunelessly, his half-moon spectacles perched on a perspiring nose, he would prink and prim some lowly clerk's headgear, as outside the fog came down and Labour Cabinet Ministers were pelted with offal by indignant ex-RAF squadron leaders selling matches and jumping beans.

Every so often the shop bell would jangle and in would walk the mighty and the humble alike. In this way I met Mr Max Miller and Mr Gordon Richards, but also Mr Perceval of the Bonds Department of Barclay's Dominion, Colonial and Overseas, surely one of the most lettered men ever to leave Enfield Lock. His monumental work on Chladni figures sticks in my mind to this very day. It may just be necessary to inform my readers that Chladni figures are made from bowing the edge of a glass or steel plate strewn with sand. The dispersal of the sand between node and antinode is an early experiment in sound. Mr Perceval's wife, though she had seen the process and the results, was – and I will say this no matter what the consequence – an enemy to science. The poor man would often call in at the shop, a piece of sticking plaster on his forehead, or with his spectacles taped up.

'At certain frequencies, Mr Jenks,' he would whisper with his habitual half-smile, 'sound can destabilise matter. Opera singers shattering wine glasses. But I think I can do better. I think I could shatter opera singers. Martha has agreed to let me have the Anderson shelter in the garden as a home and workshop. We shall have to see what we can do.'

I often wonder what became of him and his unlovely wife Martha.

But to return to our story proper.

'I am having some cards printed,' the proprietor said one day. 'And with them, I want you to walk about the City with a confident spring to your step, wearing that trilby there, left unclaimed by the Provost of King's College, Cambridge. Your task, Jenks, will be to advertise the name and services of Walter Oliphant. Whenever you see a man in a shabby hat, hit him with the card and an invitation to call in for a consultation. You must appear busy. You must imagine yourself hurrying from one place of international finance to another. Giving the punter the card must seem a form of freemasonry, almost. Do you get my drift?'

'Exactly and to the last detail, Chief.'

I have never enquired to find out who the Provost of King's was who had so carelessly left his headgear with us in 1938, but he was certainly of colossal brain size – or, if not that, cranium. Not even my protruding ears could hold up this giant trilby. I was forced to roll a *Daily Telegraph* into a false brow and then jam the hat down over it. Mr Oliphant provided a rubberised mackintosh, and so accoutred I would march about the commerical quarters of London, passing out cards and giving explanations of myself to the police.

'Sarge, I have caught this young nut walking about the St Paul's area impersonating David Niven and going on something awful about Pluto.'

'Oh yus? Pluto was it? My dog's not unlike Pluto.'

'I suppose your dog comes round only once in every 248 years,' I piped. 'And it would also be true, would it, that your dog is about the fifteenth stellar magnitude and therefore not visible in small telescopes?'

There followed what a novelist would call a pregnant pause.

'I would like you to know,' the Sergeant said at last with heavy emphasis, 'that my brother Jack crawled on his belly halfway up Monte Cassino for the likes of you. Take off them newspaper leggings, you horrible thing. Bumstead, have a look in the old box of tricks and see if you can find this streak o' widdle a pair of trews.'

Thus, as always, the bumbling incompetence of the police. Arrested for wearing newspaper leggings and rehearsing aloud the salient features of a planet, I was discharged within the hour in a Ghurka bandsman's trousers reaching halfway between knee and ankle, and told to repeat a thousand times 'I am a very naughty little boy'. The reader must judge which was more likely to breach public order.

It gradually began to dawn on me that Oliphant was in a highly select trade. I have read that those who make millions have the estimable commercial virtue of never taking no for an answer. I am afraid to say I was all too quickly worn down by ridicule and refusal. My steps faltered and in time I gave away the cards to almost anyone, provided they looked meek enough.

In this way I met – but all too briefly – Gandhi.

As I have indicated, we met when the celebrated home weaver had his shoe caught in tramlines at Ludgate Circus. It was hardly past three in the afternoon but a fog was building up. I sized up the situation immediately and cramming the mighty trilby more firmly on to my head darted out into the traffic. The Mahatma accepted Mr Oliphant's business card with a hasty *pranam* before the Blackfriar's tram scattered us. I had a fleeting vision of the world's most famous Indian hopping on one leg before being caught a glancing blow myself by a Charrington's dray.

'Lord love us, it's you again, Jenksie,' PC Bumstead said, looming over me in cape and helmet.

'Never mind me! I think Gandhi has just been run over by the Blackfriar's tram.'

'Oh, yes,' Bumstead murmured comfortably. 'Gandhi, eh? What happened? It wasn't old Tommy Trinder driving the tram was it?'

The crude humour of the ignorant and unlettered. Yet herein lies a curious sequel. The only person ever actually to visit Mr Oliphant as a consequence of his advertising drive was indeed Gandhi. When I returned limping to headquarters, there he was, engaged in candlelit conversation with the Chief. Oliphant was considerably bemused.

'Where is your hat?' he cried.

'And where is your heart?' the Indian riposted.

'That is beside the point.'

'There also you will find my hat.'

To be sure, the partition of India was but a year away, and Gandhi may have been less than fully engaged with the problem he had set the exasperated Mr Oliphant. When I arrived, the two men were at a complete linguistic and philosophical cross-roads.

'You know what a hat is, don't you?' the goodhearted proprietor was pleading.

The lawyer in Gandhi was sharply exercised by the question.

'If I admit to that, what is the consequence? I know what a hat is, yes. I know what a pair of braces is. I know what is a shoe tree, coat hanger, shaving brush, walking stick and collar stud. But why are you asking me all this? Your young assistant here has given me your card, and I present myself accordingly.'

'Take this gentleman next door, Jenks, and buy him a cup of tea.'

We repaired thence. Gandhi regarded me with kindly good nature.

'You look pale, my young friend. You are possibly eating the wrong things. What is that mark under your nose.'

'A false moustache, Mr Gandhi.'

'And the trousers you are wearing?'

'Belonged originally to a Ghurka bandsman.'

He pushed his wire-frame glasses more firmly on to his nose and shook his head from side to side.

'Your young life would benefit from change. Prayer, possibly. But at all events, you need help. Go into the country. Discover yourself by becoming a pilgrim upon the road. Find a hat that fits you. Stay away from all meat. Drink only water. All these things will assist you.'

'May I ask you – '

Gandhi held up his hand.

'I would much rather you didn't.'

In this way I found myself walking through Epping Forest the very next Saturday, acting upon Gandhi's excellent advice, though still sporting the Provost of King's trilby, for it was raining lightly. Additionally, I had with me a gas mask case filled with tomato sandwiches, and a bow and arrow, fashioned from a piece of string and a length of hornbeam. My mind was childishly indulging in fantasies of Robin Hood. The principle of robbing the rich to pay the poor was – and remains – an attractive economic policy with me. I did not know at the time, as I strode the greensward, etc., that we should come to the even more popular formulation of robbing the poor to pay the rich – but that is another matter. The reader must picture me, half man, half child, marching about in Epping Forest, loosing off arrows at selected targets. A week of vegetarianism and tap water had slightly unhinged me.

I became aware – as can happen in remote woodland – that Someone was watching me, a realisation that gave rise to an unpleasant crawling sensation in the nape of the neck and elsewhere. Screened by birches, I saw a mounted figure. If I turned my back and made in a different direction, I could hear the muffled patter of hooves in the fallen leaves. There was the occasional jingle of harness and I fancy once or twice the accidental twang of a stringed musical instrument. The noted Japanese director Kurosawa has captured this well, on other subjects. But this was before his time. My explanation was simpler. Had I in some way raised the ghost of Alan A'Dale? Had some warp of time placed me back in the reign of Richard I? The unpleasant crawling sensation intensified. My enormous trilby fell down over my eyes. I raised my hands in a very anachronistic gesture of surrender.

'I pray thee unstring thy bow, if that thou hast,' I cried to the interior of the Provost's hat, but loud enough to be heard by the horseman. 'I am naught but a varlet, Claude yclept of the Ham of Beck, or Becken. Have pity, therefore, if ye be of the Sheriff's party.'

'What's in the bag?' a voice growled.

'Bread and . . .'

Now of course, as every reader knows, the earliest reference to the tomato in European literature is in the herbal of Matthiolous of 1554. I was thus in somewhat of a quandary. I felt confident to pass off the notion of a sandwich to any agent of the Sheriff of Nottingham (as being, for example, an accidental juxtaposition of bread and filling) but much less certain of explaining the concept tomato sandwich. If the City of London police balked at Pluto, what hope of the tomato before the Sheriff of Nottingham?

'Bread and what, son? And take off that durned hat. Come out from under.'

There, standing before me, in dazzling white with matching fringes, his holster low, his chin high, was not the black-hearted Sheriff's man, but the incomparable legend of the West, Roy Rogers!

And, a little to one side, Trigger!

Each smiled good-naturedly. It was an even greater shock than meeting Monty.

I fainted clean away.

'The subject is a young man, employed as a felt hat steamer by a City firm, who was found in Epping Forest under the delusion he had met the film actor Roy Rogers. According to his testimony he had been sent there by M. K. Gandhi.'

'Roy Rogers had been sent there by Gandhi, sir?'

Dr McFadyean gazed gloomily on the young houseman, Owen.

'No, David. Roy Rogers wasn't there, if ye catch my drift. Roy Rogers lives in Hollywood, or somewhere like that. I don't know for sure where he lives, but I think we can say, with some medical certainty in the matter, he was not in Epping Forest last Saturday morning. But our young friend here *was* there. Did Mr Gandhi tell you to lay off the meat, young man?'

'Yessir.'

'And had you maybe pulled a few wee mushrooms as you wandered along? Was that it, possibly?'

'That was my first explanation,' Owen said.

'Well now,' McFadyean said, patting my hand. 'I've asked my wee wifie to look you out some breeks and a couple of golf sweaters. You can maybe make use of this tam as well – do you not want to say goodbye to that big hattie job of yours?'

'It belongs to the Provost of King's College, Cambridge.'

'Does it now, does it now,' McFadyean mused. He turned to young Dr Owen. 'In your opinion, David, would the wee man be any better off if he *had* seen Roy Rogers?'

From Garnett, Rosenwald, Fitz and Uhlenlake, *Roy Rogers, the Man, the Myth and the Movie Star* (New York, 1957): 'In November of 1946, Roy flew to London, England, to meet his many fans. He stayed at the Dorchester Hotel but several times took the opportunity to slip away from the admiring Britishers. "Guess I just saddled up Trigger and rode," Roy explained to His Majesty King George, who was anxious to know what he had seen of England's green and pleasant land.'

– Seven –

There used to be at Waterloo station, and for all I know there still is, a news theatre, of the kind that showed cartoons and what are called in the film industry shorts, as well as a badly edited and half-digested programme of news. Why this should have had its place at Waterloo I do not know. Nor can I say for what purpose others have made use of such a facility. Their reasons cannot be entirely idle, for it takes some steel in the soul to sit in a cinema at three in the afternoon watching the antics of small animals speaking American.

On this occasion my own purpose was crystal clear. My London period, as I think of it, was altogether in question. I had not gone to the cinema for recreation, but to apply for the job of projectionist. Seven long years had passed since first I set foot in the Marylebone Public Library and I was at last beginning to falter in my desire to be a great writer, or indeed a wordsmith of any kind. My historical novel on Adalbert, second Bishop of Prague, had gone the rounds of publishing houses without success. (It had also gone the rounds of the Circle Line for over a month when I accidentally misplaced it on the way home from a lecture by Stephen King-Hall.) The only slight encouragement I received was a charming note from Victor Gollancz, commending the martyrdom of the Saint, which occurs in the last chapter. With his eye for a taut ms, VG noted that the event had come, for him personally, not a moment too soon.

It being quickly established by the management that I had no first-hand knowledge of cinema projection, I was shown the door. It is a curiosity of the architecture of such places that there are stairs and corridors in excess of strictly utilitarian requirements. I tramped about for a while in poorly-lit passages, now descending three carpeted steps, now ascending four more, until at last finding myself part of the unwilling audience to 'Look At Life No.27: Bagpipes.' It was a sombre experience, even for those few who appreciate the music of the humourless Picts. However, the thrust of the story is this: all at once my attention was drawn to a commotion some few rows in front of me. I thought at first it was a case of mayhem – perhaps some traveller stabbed to death for his ticket to a far-flung town on the south coast. The case was quite otherwise. A small white-haired man with bushy eyebrows had been taken by a fit of cramp to his thigh and had plunged in agony to the floor of the auditorium.

That man was of course Albert Einstein, then at the height of his powers. I do not mean then – *then* he was crying out in several languages and pretty much incapacitated. But I knew him instantly for who he was and, making my way to him, tugged off my balaclava as a form of doffing my hat to genius.

'I believe you are Albert Einstein, famed mathematician, physicist, and native of Ulm. Author of *Die Grundlage der Allgemeinen Relativitätstheorie* and, moreover – '

'Young man,' Einstein interrupted, seizing my hand. 'I am in the extremes of agony here. Be so good as to assist me from the theatre.'

Einstein, as I soon discovered, was of quite preternatural powers of mental concentration. Where you or I might have crawled up the aisle with no more thought than to cure our cramp and be off home, he remembered that he had with him a cake and an umbrella, without which he would not leave. While he lay in the aisle, therefore, his hat jammed on his head any which way, perforce must I crawl about in the dark, looking for the learned philosopher's belongings.

'*Ach, das verdammt dudelsakmusik!*' he shouted the while.

The upshot of all this was that I found the cake, but not the umbrella. Hoisting the diminutive thinker on to my back and clutching the cake, I strode from the scene of his embarrassment, determined to make further acquaintance of such a famous man. We went to the buffet for a cup of tea. There Einstein remained restless and chafing.

He wanted to know if his umbrella would be handed in to Railway Lost Property, and to know this he must first know whether the cinema was party to that estimable organisation; or whether through some quirk of the lease, or perhaps some Act of Parliament governing places of entertainment, the umbrella would be handed in at a police station. I promised we would get the facts set straight as soon as we had refreshed ourselves.

'But tell me,' I said, 'how you came to be watching Loony Toons in company with the rest of us? What drove you there, esteemed Nobel Prize-winner? What accident of fate set you down among us?'

It turned out he had a more mundane reason than I – he was on his way to see his sister-in-law.

'And that explains the cake!' I cried heartily.

His deep eyes darkened. 'In what way?'

'The cake is a present for your sister-in-law, or perhaps your brother.'

He thought this over. At last he allowed there was a reasonable presumption in what I had said. But the truth was more interesting. It seemed that Einstein had made an arrangement with a mathematical colleague, whose name I cannot now remember, to deliver the cake as the train passed through a certain station.

'A pleasant opportunity to greet an old friend and exchange notes in the few moments that the train pauses,' I suggested.

'On the contrary,' he said, a little stiffly. 'The train does not stop there. My friend and his family will be on the platform with a stretched tennis net, and my work is done when the train passes and I hurl the cake out of the window.'

He asked me for another cup of tea and loan of a pound, to tide him over for the weekend. I did this, and felt emboldened to tell him of my book.

'What book?'

I began with Adalbert's birth in AD 957, and my conjectures on the character of his parents, about whom little is known. After a few minutes, Einstein jumped up, exclaiming noisily that he had not realised the time, must make haste to catch his train, etc. We exchanged addresses. He gave his as care of the Royal Automobile Club. I went home and wrote down every word that he had spoken and drew a sketch of him from memory, adding the inscription 'Albert Einstein at Waterloo' and the date. And there the matter might have rested. It almost certainly would have rested there, had he repaid the small loan I had made him. But when after a week had passed and there was no cheque or note of thanks, I pressed the trousers to a brown suit I had in those days, and took myself to the headquarters of the RAC.

'The gentleman is not a member,' some functionary said, after checking through a book of names.

'Would you be so kind as to check again?'

For answer, the man slammed the book shut under my very nose.

'And what makes you think this gentleman you met in the news cinema was Albert Einstein? And even if he was, what was he doing borrowing a pound from you?'

An aside: I have often come across this attitude. Even quite learned and in all other respects sophisticated people find it hard to imagine the famous as having the same sort of life as you or I. The famous take their shoes to be mended; they go to the library, or visit the butcher. They may have the aura of fame about them, but their lives are as frail – or as robust – as yours or mine. I shall never forget meeting the old Duke of Norfolk at Sheringham, when he and I were waiting for a kipper stall to open. He was planning to send some boxed kippers to a distant relative in Malaya, as it then was, I to a young lady in Cirencester. We shared an umbrella.

However, to return to my narrative. I was ejected from the RAC after heated words on both sides, and paced the streets of London, musing on the vagaries of life and the unfathomable complexity of human nature. My steps led me, I know not how, to Welbeck Street and there to my great astonishment who should I see in the window of an antique shop but the object of my enquiry! I entered at once.

Einstein was in a much jollier frame of mind. His trip to the country had set him up, he said. He stayed longer than he had planned, and had even turned out for a scratch team got up by his hosts, in a tight football friendly against the Coal and Coke Depot.

'And now, after those exertions, here you are, buying a grandfather clock.'

He patted my hand with great good humour.

'You have a writer's eye,' he smiled. 'I am indeed about to purchase this fine old timepiece, and you can do me the greatest service by helping me to a cab with it. It is a gift, a presentation.'

'Like the cake,' I suggested archly. He furrowed his brow for a moment and then remembered the cake he had flung from the train. His eyes twinkled.

'Would you like to know the outcome of the cake story?'

'With all my heart!'

'I threw it out at the wrong station! A lamentable thing, my dear friend. A lady in a fur coat caught it. Whether she understood my hurried explanation, or whether the words were snatched away on the wind as we hurtled past, I cannot say.'

'Incredible!'

'Hardly. Hardly incredible. But interesting.'

It was getting towards the time of night when cabs were hard to find, and Einstein proposed – and

I accepted – that we carry the clock to Oxford Street, and take it down on the Central Line.

'After which,' he insisted, 'you must consider yourself discharged from all obligation. From that point, I shall make my way as best I can. I have managed before with worse problems.'

And so we set off, the clock chiming gently between us, as the envious home-goers stared – Einstein the world shaper, the most famous brainbox of the century, and marching in step, with only the length of a clock between us, a young and eager Jenks. We were assisted part of the way to Oxford Circus by a roistering crowd that included C. Day Lewis and Robert Helpmann, who had just left the BBC on their way to a badminton match against a House of Commons Select team. I introduced Einstein to our companions and he told the story of the cake again, with embellished details, while accepting a drink from a silver hip flask that was passed around.

'And who is this young man, Bert?' a genial lad enquired.

'This is Mr Claude Jenks, a writer and seeker after truth,' Einstein said with a generosity I shall never forget. All present shook hands with me, and I loaned Helpmann the price of a meal for two, as he was going to supper later that night and had been unable to get to the banks. Day Lewis said some remarkable things.

'I never knew you were so short, Albert. It comes

as a bit of a shock to see you in the flesh like this. I think I could have coped with a taller person, but your close particularity has unsettled me.'

'Size is a relative matter,' Einstein pointed out.

'Oh yes, to be sure, no doubt of that. Mass, and all that. But I had you down in my book as a slightly . . . well, larger person.'

All well and good, but we must fain get the clock down the steps to the Underground. In the very act of saying goodbye to our sporting friends, a woman in a fur coat came out of Bourne & Hollingworth and came up to the mathematician and philosopher at a crouching half run, handbag whirling.

'Yes! You're the bloody man who threw the cake at me on Andover Station. I'd know your face anywhere.'

And such of course is fame. Einstein and I were taken, with the clock, to a police station, where the woman made out a formal complaint. We were then taken down into the cells and left to cool our heels.

'Is this the time,' I tapped with my shoe upon the wall that separated us, 'to mention the small loan I made you, which you have not repaid, perhaps through some oversight?'

There was silence while I wondered whether Einstein had ever mastered the simple language of Morse: but at last his answer came through.

'You English,' he said.

Einstein as I knew him, therefore, was sharp as a razor, let there be no mistake about it – and with an unworldliness of a sort that sits well with our cliché of the famous. I would place him with Olivier for niggardliness in small matters. The great actor and I once spent an entire evening in a pub off Charlotte Street, betting on whether the banknotes in his wallet were of odd or even numbers, before it was pointed out to me by the kindly publican that he carried nothing but odds, and was indeed known in that pub as Odds Larry.

I last saw Einstein being bundled into a police car, with his clock, and whisked away to some other venue.

'But I am still owed a pound,' I cried after the departing genius.

'Yes, well, you won't see that again, my old matey,' a grizzled constable smirked. He escorted me as far as Liberty's, and then, with a jocular punch in the kidneys, bade me goodnight.

– *Eight* –

Last night I was reading about the Old Man of the Mountains, whom Marco Polo almost met on his way to Peking. I am very sorry he made no real effort to track this interesting man down, any more than he went out of his way to find the tree under which Alexander the Great sat, which the members of his caravan assured him was still standing, and grown to an immense size in the intervening centuries. But we have to remember that Polo was a beardless youth and in the company of his father and his uncle, who had heard all these stories before. They wanted to cut along to Peking and re-greet their old friend Kublai Khan, who sat waiting for them in the summer palace of Shang-tu, the Xanadu of the poem by Coleridge. It was hardly likely that the two grizzled merchants would pay much heed to the suggestions of the impressionable teenager, Marco. I fell asleep with the mental picture of them pelting the lad with camel droppings.

However, this reading set off a train of thought that has persisted all morning. We shall go no further than Paris by this train, it is true, but the circumstances may be of interest.

It was Edith Sitwell who first suggested I should gain experience of life by travel. We met in the little tea bar that used to be sited at the entrance to South Kensington Tube Station. I had come from a study of dung beetles at the Natural History Museum, and she, as she explained, was just back from National Hunt racing at Plumpton. Miss Sitwell was kind enough to enquire in a general sort of way about my interest in *Geotrupes Stercorarius*.

'Is the dung the fascination?' she asked, her eyes screwed up against the cigarette smoke that wreathed her features and rolled round her incredible velvet hat.

'Rather, dear poetess, the fact that the species is often found on its back, its legs waving in the air. I wonder how this could be of any possible help to it, in a Darwinian scheme of things.'

'What a strange young man you are,' she murmured, wiping her unforgettable nose with a none too clean thumb. It turned out that she had her own vexations with animal creation. An each-way double on the third and fourth at Plumpton had let her down badly, thanks to the running of a horse called Idle Jack.

By Miss Sitwell's account of things, this was a horse of extraordinary stupidity, as well as of idleness. The first leg of the double (and here I freely confess I had as much idea of what she was talking about then as I do now in the retelling of it) had romped home at 33 to 1. All that was required of Idle Jack in the next race was that he came at least third in a field of ten. There was fog at Plumpton, and as the field passed the stands for the first time, Miss Sitwell's selection was on the bridle in sixth place. The horses disappeared into the fog. The distinguished poet was, as she put it, just getting her chops round a ham sandwich when Idle Jack reappeared, running counter-clockwise and with the jockey helpless to do anything about it. Once again it disappeared into the fog. There was an oppressive silence. After a while came the thunder of hooves as the race proper concluded. Of Idle Jack, nothing.

'Not a peep,' Miss Sitwell declared, putting the teaspoons and an ashtray into her capacious handbag. 'The idle little sod had vanished off the face of the earth.'

She suddenly reached and seized my hand in a vice-like grip.

'Or so we thought,' she whispered, with her instinct for dramatic timing, well evinced in her collection *The Canticle of the Rose*, just then newly published.

In the sixth race, where a finish was being hotly contested between Luck o' the Irish and Bold

Heresy, Idle Jack once again appeared from the right, this time without the jockey, but towing a member of the St John's Ambulance Brigade. All three horses and the luckless first-aid man collided twenty yards from the finishing post.

'I think I have the rough gist of it,' I said, staring into her glittering eyes.

'Oh you do, do you? Well it doesn't compare to the study of the dung beetle, I grant you that. But it spoilt my racing. It ruined my day out.'

'That I can well imagine.'

She stared at me without warmth, picking her teeth with a bus ticket.

'In five minutes the pubs'll be open,' she muttered.

I have never been a great pub-goer, not since singing 'You've Got the Whole World in Your Hands' at the Star and Garter, Droitwich, a story I do not intend to tell here; but needs must we leave the tea bar and repair to a pub Miss Sitwell knew, where she drank something called Snowballs, and I a half of bitter. After I had paid for half a dozen Snowballs and a gin to wash the taste out of her mouth, Miss Sitwell advised me to travel.

'You want to get the dung beetle out of your system. Get it completely behind you. Visit places, see people.'

'I suppose your own creative juices have been stirred in that way.'

'You evil-minded little swine,' Dame Edith

shrilled. 'My creative juices are my own, and if my brothers were in here, they'd bash your head in with an iron bar for a filthy remark like that.'

'Well, where do you suggest I travel?' I asked hastily.

'The way *you* treat women? Paris.'

And with that she staggered to the dart board, on the invitation of Denis Compton and Freddie Mills, whose local it seemed to be, and began an erratic game of 501, a pound the first leg, a pound the second, and a fiver the match.

The opportunity to take advantage of her advice came very soon after. A man I met in Selfridges proposed, and I accepted, that I should go to Paris and collect a small parcel on his behalf. The parcel contained art-work for a new magazine he was contemplating, to be published from an address in Victoria. He would go himself, etc., but he must consider his old mother, to whom he was devoted, and whom he had promised to take to the Ideal Home Exhibition. Accordingly I set off for the city of romance with an address written on a scrap of paper, some sandwiches, and a copy of *Madame Bovary* with which to while away the hours.

I pass over the uneventful crossing, the train journey to the Gare du Nord, the discovery that the francs given to me in London turned out to be pre-Revolutionary roubles, and all the rest of it, and come to the meat of the story. The man I was to meet, from whom I was to collect the package, was none other than Pablo Picasso! I recognised him instantly from his bald head and striped Breton sweater.

'*Ah, cher maître,*' I exclaimed joyfully. '*Quelle sensass!*'

Picasso peered round the door at me with caution.

'Did Arthur de Londres send you?' he asked.

'Of the magazine *Thrust*.'

'Wears a camel-hair coat?'

'With an aged mother he calls the duchess.'

Picasso nodded and unhooked the chain.

'*Entrez,*' he said.

I was ushered into a room devoted, it would be true to say, to art. All thought of the actual purpose of my visit was forgotten. Picasso was cooking meatballs at an ancient stove, and there was a bed, of sorts, against one wall. But the rest of the space was littered with sketches, photographs and a few paintings. As can be imagined, my eye was hungry for detail. The master swept up the work nearest me with a nervous gesture.

'You weren't followed here by a short man in a mac? Walks with a limp? Chain-smokes Gauloises?'

'I don't think so. I see you are in a figurative mode at the moment. Little of cubism here, *maître*.'

Picasso asked me directly and boldly to mind my own business. Without inviting me to partake, he turned his meatballs out on to a chipped enamel plate and ate them, standing up the while. Somewhere someone was practising the tuba.

'Got any money?' he asked.

'Quite a lot, but not negotiable in France.'

I showed him the roubles and he laughed mirthlessly. Socially, we were at an impasse. It was galling in the extreme to be in the presence of genius and find that the hour was by no means calling forth the man.

'Claudine'll be here in a bit,' he said doubtfully.

'I was on the point of asking you about "*Les Demoiselles D'Avignon*",' I said, after another excruciating silence.

'That's all been cleared up,' Picasso said.

More silence.

And now I come to a significant aspect of these present memoirs. To explain, I must take you back for a moment to Marco Polo. As is well known, Marco, or Polo, call him what you will, did not actually write his own account of his travels. Only a year after his return to Venice, the traveller very unwisely fell foul of the Genoese, was captured and thrown into gaol. There he met by chance one Rustichello, a literary hack from Pisa, who suggested to him that he send to Venice for his notes and that they crack on with a book of his adventures. Thus, without Rustichello, no book. I may say I often think of this unfortunate man with more emotion than I do Marco himself. At the time of his imprisonment the great traveller was thirty-two and called by his pals *Il Millioni*. About the Pisan wordsmith who actually got him to sit down and say where he had been and what he had seen, we know nothing save that he got small thanks for his task. (Polo even lost the original manuscript after getting out of clink – what a find *that* would be.)

I mention all this because of what follows. I think we all know with what glory the name of Picasso is covered, while that of Jenks has been until now obscured by ignominy. But the events of that chill and misty night in Paris, once they have been told in proper sequence, will I think astonish the world.

After what seemed hours of gloomy Catalan silence, Picasso electrified me by suggesting we go out and rob a *tabac* at gunpoint. At first I laughed it off, but he said he was desperate for some cash, someone called Zazie La Folle had loaned him the gun, he was tired of risking the jug for his drawings and anyway he did not think he could spend another night in the room we sat in without going barking mad.

This aspect of Picasso is, you will note, not touched upon by Sir Roland Penrose or others, who at this time would have him the richest painter who ever lived, and choosing frantically between mistresses and houses while being besieged by galleries and collectors worldwide.

'Alright,' Picasso said. 'We'll do it this way. You stay here and wait for Claudine. Meet me at the Porte des Lilas. She'll know where to look.'

My pleadings were in vain. The great painter snatched up the gun Zazie La Folle had loaned him, pulled on a beret and was gone. *Dites donc*, as they say in France. I wrapped myself in a blanket and sat down to wait for Claudine.

Towards nine, there was a knock at the door. I opened it expecting to find the lissome model depicted in all her naked innocence on the scattered sheets of the master's scribblings – but instead was faced with a very large man in a camel-hair coat, the brother to that worn by Arthur in London. By way of introduction, this scented bully lifted me by one hand and sat me down on the stove, which, while not red hot, was not entirely bereft of warmth either.

'You're late with the drawings,' Monsieur Camel-hair croaked. 'The patron don't like that.'

'Allow me to explain – ' I began. The bully pushed his index finger deep into my nostril, causing blinding tears. Meanwhile, my cord trousers were beginning to smoulder.

'He wants three good drawings by ten tonight. The real McCoy. They better be. Otherwise he's going to cut your hands off.'

'This is a case of mistaken identity. My name is Claude Jenks, and I am a British passport holder.'

'I never met you before,' the bully admitted. 'But if you don't stop messing people about you won't have no hands to hold your passport, will you? So get going. Three good strong drawings in your old style. Not this rubbish on the floor. The real stuff. Or else. I'll be back.'

And with that, he withdrew.

Here was a pretty pass. Picasso out robbing a *tabac*, no sign of Claudine, no sign of the package I was supposed to take back to London, and a pocketful of worthless and by now charred roubles. I confess I was, for a few moments, panicked. The fog that had bedevilled the meeting at Plumpton had reached Paris, and was licking at the grimy windowpanes. I had eaten nothing but a cheese roll since leaving Victoria at nine that morning.

Picasso – and here I play Rustichello to his Polo without shame or embarrassment – can count himself lucky, wherever he is now, that I knew enough about his work and its periods to help him out of a tight spot that February evening. Without Jenks, he might have ended his career with two false hands, learning how to pick up matchboxes in some occupational therapy unit out at St Cloud or somewhere. Finding some paper to hand, and the stub of a pencil, I set to. I took as my subject none other than Dame Edith herself, partly because of the striking possibilities offered to cubism by her nose, which I had never before considered in that light. On her head she wore the Doge's beret she had sported at our meeting. And rearing itself up in a corner of the picture, the lips drawn back from the teeth, I added Idle Jack, in sketch form.

Now my muse was on fire! My second drawing was of the St John's Ambulance man being towed past the stands. Here I borrowed a little from

Chagall, to give a dreamy energy to the work: the first-aid man flew overhead as the three horses collided in a mass of triangular planes. In the third study, I chose to represent Dame Edith, Denis Compton and Freddie Mills *en fête champêtre*. Bold radial lines suggested the dartboard in place of the tablecloth. Idle Jack's rump was to be seen right of frame. The execution of all these works was rapid, vivid, impassioned. I signed and dated them in the bottom right hand corner and left them where the bully would be sure to find them. Without waiting for the mysterious and unpunctual Claudine, I left, groping my way through the fog.

There are two further details to this story, one of which does me no credit. Outside Le Crillon, I bought a handful of hot chestnuts from a short-sighted itinerant vendor, paying for them with the charred remains of the roubles. This has lain long upon my conscience. I wrote to Sartre on the matter shortly after returning to England, asking for his philosophical comment. I received a reply from Simone de Beauvoir, saying he was busy.

The other matter brings us back, so to speak, to 1296, the gaol in Genoa and the good-hearted Rustichello. My sympathy with that fair Pisan was always strong, but enormously enhanced a few years after this Paris escapade when I opened a book on Picasso and found, as Plate 78, my rendering of Dame Edith, Denis Compton and Freddie Mills, in the possession of the University of Minnesota, the

Kenneth Lowden Collection. I at once wrote to the Keeper of the Collection, with a copy to the Syndics of the University. Their reply was less than satisfactory. No word of mine could alter their opinion that, as a Ms Shelly-Anne Bundy asserted, on behalf of the Senate Board, 'the Picasso we have is just dandy and we know of no reason to doubt its provenance'. I wrote again to Ms Bundy, explaining that at the time the drawing was made, Picasso was out robbing a *tabac* with what appeared to be a .45 Webley.

This time the reply came from a Professor Guttmann, of the Department of Psychiatry. He wondered why I had mentioned the hand gun, a detail he found especially revealing. He was doing a study of people who made up stories with big guns in them, and would welcome a correspondence.

Marco Polo died in 1324 and was buried in the church of San Lorenzo. It goes without saying that we cannot discover from the standard works of reference when Rustichello died. As I have mentioned, not without a certain sympathetic bitterness, Marco Polo, *Il Millioni*, took the credit for the success of *The Description of the World*: the Pisan took the blame. One of the most insulting things said about his Ms is that it is written in bad French with many awkward Italianisms. I hope he wrote to Polo about that. I hope he had more success than I with Picasso.

– *Nine* –

I was once taken to dinner by the great American crooner Mr Elvis Presley. The venue was an unusual one – we met by the side of the road near the modest but sturdy Lincolnshire town of Spalding. I had good reason to be there, for I had chanced across a report of a case of poltergeistism in a national newspaper and had written offering my services to the owner of the property so afflicted, a retired RAF officer called Broome. If it does not impede the thrust of my narrative, I should like to say a few words about this Broome.

It is not in my nature to draw attention to mental failings in my fellow man, but I do have to say that Broome was, by any measurement of sanity, nudging the red. To travel to Lincolnshire at all is no mean feat, and as it chanced I had decided upon the visit in distant Ilfracombe. Suffice it to say that I arrived at Tally-Ho Cottage, after a four-day cycle ride, weary of limb and in need of the basic elements of hospitality. I had not counted on being greeted by a former bomber pilot wearing an old-fashioned tin colander on his head. Such was Broome when he opened the door to me.

'Come ye in, come ye in,' he cried, pulling the haversack from my back. 'We'll have a swift one here and then down to the pub, what say you?'

'I believe you are troubled by poltergeists,' I said, believing it best to come to the point immediately. Broome tapped his metal hat.

'Dear old lad,' he said. 'It's been a nightmare. The stuff has been simply whizzing about. *Whizzing* about. Clocks, knives, those fire tongs there – they were my mother's, God bless her – everything. Damn blizzard, some nights. What's your hat size? I may have a saucepan to fit.'

You have the general drift of the man here. Broome's disease was an incurable gung-ho jollity. It came out during the course of a long evening that he had been discharged from the RAF.

'And do you know why, old chap? For always looking on the bright side. I was a very not-to-worry sort of pilot – joined in the war, stayed on for the peace, but was never cut out to be a penguin. Bumph, desk-wallahs backbiting all the time, weary sort of life. I drank, I don't say I didn't. A few beers, game of skittles maybe, shove a crate in the back of the old Sprite, finish up with a sing-song.'

Sadly, all these pleasures were taken alone. For a

year or so the RAF turned a blind eye. Then one night Broome was seen climbing into a Vulcan, with the intention of popping over to Berlin to see what Jerry was up to. The year was 1965.

'About the poltergeist phenomena,' I prompted him.

'Started about a year ago. Sitting watching the old goggle-box – *twang*! Damn bread knife whistles past. Look up, immediately on the *qui vive* as it were, *whoosh*! A tin of pilchards from that cupboard over there. Used to keep m'pilchards in that cupboard. Not any more, old lad! Not any more!'

We kept vigil for three nights. It goes without saying that not a single thing changed position in that cottage, unless it were thrown by Broome as a rather silly prank. We must have presented a strange sight, he in his colander, me with a preserving pan on my head. We were each furnished with tennis rackets to strike away the attacks when they came.

'Funny thing,' Broome said at last. 'Chaps must be frightened of you. Good juju. You wouldn't consider bunking up here with me for a few months? Just until the thing blows over?'

'That is a kind offer,' I said. 'But my steps lead elsewhere.'

''Nuff said,' the pilot muttered, with the first signs of having any melancholy in his brain to draw upon. We parted friends, I hope.

However, to Mr Elvis Presley, the successful

American singer. A few miles after leaving Tally-Ho Cottage, the faithful Rudge, with the thirty-two-inch wheels and c-section mudguards, the Loosemore cotter pins and Stanwick and Jackson panniers, wherein I kept my traveller's library – the Rudge, as I say, seized. The problem was a wand of willow wrapped round the back cogwheel. I was in no hurry, the weather was clement, and I upturned the machine by the side of the road to effect a repair.

I have to say that my knowledge of Mr Elvis Presley was slight, and has remained so, in respect to his many recordings and films. Mrs Strutt is a loyal fan and assures me he was in his day a very popular entertainer. I had some dim idea that a person of that name existed, who broadcasted from time to time, but Elvis, as he soon enough begged me to call him, could have passed by on that lonely Lincolnshire road without a second glance from me. Instead he hove to, cut the ignition to the tractor he was driving, and walked back towards me.

'You know who I am, don't you.' he said, with a rather foolish smirk. 'I'm Elvis, me.'

'Mr Mee, do you have a long-shafted screwdriver you can lend me?'

'Not Mee, Elvis! Elvis Presley!'

'Ah,' I said, culling my recollection of youths in the public eye who combed their hair ceaselessly.

'Give me wahn fo' ma money,' the youngster sang. The penny dropped.

'What are you doing driving a tractor?' I asked the singer. 'And on the outskirts of Spalding?'

He had ready answer.

'I gotta get away from all the hassle, man. The people buggin' me, wanting ma clothes, locks of ma hair, it ain't right what they're doin' to muh. Mah mind is blown.'

'And so, you are for the present incognito.'

'Doan know what it means, but it sure sounds purty,' the baby-faced crooner smiled. 'Lessun you mean that old Cognito back o' Memphis on the country road.'

I make some effort to render the vowels of this extraordinary young man for good reason. I certainly did not, but be assured Elvis *did* consider himself to be in front of the cameras the whole time I was with him. I have seldom met a more theatrical human being – and here I include as measurement Miss Hermione Gingold, with whom I had the honour to share a taxi in Hastings one New Year's Eve. In the case of Miss Gingold, there was a certain arch quality. I found Elvis, by comparison, extremely hard-going.

And here I interrupt myself again briefly: Mrs Strutt has just burst in upon me, flushed from indulgence in her own home-made wine, a vile tincture labelled Elderberry, Banana Etcetera, that has once or twice before fanned the flames of her impudence.

'I won't hear a word said against him,' the poor

woman raved. 'He's my hero. And don't you go saying he's dead. He's not dead, he's working in a Tesco's in Birmingham. And he's hopping mad. But not as much as he will be when he hears you've been shoving your oar in.'

'Mrs Strutt, you are interjecting a note of cliché here, an element of low comedic buffoonery that I do not actually wish my work to entertain.'

'I'll give you buffoonery! You'll get the working end of my broom across your earhole and we'll see how much that entertains you!'

'I think,' I said silkily, 'you have just made my point!'

She made an approximate and wheezing attempt at sitting down, her old face flushed.

'So I'm not good enough for your damn book, is that it?'

'Mrs Strutt, I have explained before – '

'Not good enough for your la-di-da London publishing cronies that you've never met and never will, with their houses and dogs and their friends called Emma.'

'I am trying,' I thundered, 'to write about Elvis Presley.'

'And what,' she thundered back, 'would you know about someone like that?'

'I met him once.'

'Oh yes. And where was that? At Gracelands, I suppose.'

'Near Spalding, as a matter of fact.'

Strutt stared at me, as well as she was able to focus on anything. 'That old tortoise of yours has more sense.' At which she flung out and went to bed. Or if not to bed, to ground. We must suppose the crash that shook the house to be her retiring for the night.

And the whole thing has left me trembling with a wild anger, an insensate rage. I do not wish Mrs Strutt to be in this book. I have no need of her Doll Tearsheet interludes. I resent and regret including her barometer, or indeed any aspect of her fatuous existence. I deplore her extraordinary capacity to unsettle any conversation with objections drawn from a wide portfolio of intellectual confusion.

I am not writing a journal! I am not a mere diarist!

This is intolerable. I must break off for hot milk and a chance to regroup.

Very well. We may return, with my full apology, to the side of the road, the hair-combing songster, the stalled Rudge and the cooling tractor. The wind is rustling the wild celery, the bees buzz in the bugloss and we may hear the chaffinch in a nearby bush. The ancient Lincolnshire loams glisten in the pale sunshine.

And here I can report to the sensation-hungry world a side to Mr Presley I have not seen mentioned elsewhere. For a children's entertainer of apparently world repute, he knew a dickens of a lot about potatoes. Whether or no he was quite the topnotch crooner he claimed, I have no way of judging, but Elvis Presley as I knew him was certainly a popular encyclopedia of this lowly but indispensable vegetable.

In many ways, it was quite impossible to hold a serious conversation with the lad, for he had a drollery that I am told was ever part of his presence. However, he showed me over the adjacent fields and clamps, singing the while and plucking at an imaginary guitar. I found him not without a louche charm. Shortly after a remark I had made about the Peruvian origins of the vegetable, the singer snatched up a tuber and sang 'Oh Spanish Eyes' to it with a colossal amount of vibrato. It was not unamusing.

'How is it you know so much about *Solanum Tuberosum?*' I asked.

'Who cares?' Elvis said with a sudden and characteristic fit of sulkiness. 'One thing that bugs me, Claude. You don't ask a single question about how it is to be rich an' famous and loved by millions. You don' ask me about ma next movie, ma incredible real pearl hand-stitched show suits and stuff, ma wimmin.'

'Well, you see, Elvis,' I joshed the youth, 'we differ profoundly in our musical taste.'

'Hell, name me someone. Just name me someone.'

'Elgar.'

'Elgar who? Just Elgar, like Dylan?'

I had no wish to engage with him on the subject of the plausible Welsh romantic, who had once borrowed five shillings from me in a cemetery. But I was saved from the cultural embarrassment of discussing a poet of any cloth with a posing American warbler by the arrival of a battered Austin Sprite, its horn playing the first bars of 'La Cucaracha'. It was of course the hapless Broome on his way to make, as he put it, town patrol of Spalding.

'Wing Commander Broome, Elvis Presley,' I said, effecting an introduction at the side of the road.

'Hullo, Barry,' Broome said. 'How are the spuds?'

Broome and I went on into Spalding, my bike arranged haphazardly in the remaining space of the Sprite and secured by plastic baling twine. The agreement struck was that we should meet Elvis later, after he had finished what he was doing with the tractor, etc.

'Mad as a March hare, that one,' Broome explained when we were safely ensconced in the back bar of the Tennyson Arms. This was a case of the pot calling the kettle black. Moreover, if Elvis were mad as a March hare, Broome was without question three sheets to the wind. He was having great trouble staying on his bar stool.

'He has a certain winsome charm, all the same,' I objected gently.

'Absolutely,' Broome barked. 'But not the full canteen of cutlery, if you take my drift. The gals love him. Boy's an out and out stoat with the womenfolk. A Big Hunk o' Love, and so forth. The Devil in Disguise. No wonder there's been Crying in the Chapel, eh?'

I wondered how to indicate to Broome that he was becoming seriously speech-impaired.

'Knew his mother, y'know,' the former pilot said with the effrontery of the intoxicated. 'She was a barmaid at the Thrope Arms. Pulled me many a pint of Adnam's in her time. Big Wendy. Solid joys and lasting pleasures there, fruit.'

'I remember reading somewhere that he started his career by making a personal record for the lady, I believe at the Memphis Recording Service.'

'He started,' Broome countered, 'by winning a talent contest just across the road here at the Kenneth Wolstenholme Community Centre. And it's more or less wrecked the lad, as you will have noticed. Harmless, I suppose, but it makes you wonder.'

Thus Broome on popular music. That evening, Elvis joined us for a snack supper at the Three Aces tea bar, a somewhat rhomboid wooden shed behind the bus station. Broome slept under the table, having lost a bet to drink his way across the spirits shelf at the Tennyson Arms. (He was undone within sight of the finish by the one-two-three of curaçao, rum and tincture of iodine, this last the landlord's idea of a joke). All in all it had been a scrappy day, and my mood inclined towards the melancholy. Elvis ate heartily of sausage, egg, beans and chips and then, sensing some sadness in the atmosphere, proposed to the room at large that he render his latest single, 'Love Letters'. To this there was mixed reception. Some of the more sombre elements of Spalding society were foregathered at the Three Aces that evening, with their wives and dogs; but there was also an admixture of young girls in grubby white sleeveless pullovers.

'Go on then, Barry, sock it to us,' cried one impudent miss, and the boy crooner jumped on to the table to render the first bars of the tune penned by Young-Heyman, who could not for a moment have imagined it reaching Spalding in quite this way when they sat down at the piano to compose it. Nor do I think it has ever had a more dramatic rendition.

Elvis got no further than the second line of the lyric when the legs of the table splayed outwards like those of a giraffe wishing to sit down; and in a twinkling of an eye the *tout ensemble* – singer, empty plates, cruet and menu card – collapsed upon the recumbent Broome. From under the wreckage, the old bomber pilot let out a terrified whoop.

'Skipper to crew, skipper to crew,' he shouted. 'We've taken a hit. I don't have control of the kite.

'Fraid this is it, chaps. Bale out, all of you. And God bless!'

Whereupon he jumped through the café window.

Poor Broome. I found out afterwards that he had undertaken initial parachute training many years earlier in a swimming bath at Blackpool. The circumstances outside Spalding bus station were somewhat different. He executed four perfect forward rolls and hit his head a nasty crack on the last arrival from Holbeach. This swerved and hit a bus shelter before running into the Gas Showrooms. So it was that the RAF did more actual damage to the town of Spalding than did the Luftwaffe, or indeed almost anyone else since the Danes last rowed up the Welland.

Of Elvis there is just a little more to be said, though not a great deal. A year or so ago, I was making my way to the incomparable seat of Lady Lowden for a bout of wits with her librarian, the good and saintly Dr Scott, when my eye was caught by a poster advertising an Elvis Spectacular. It proved to be in the grounds of Dexter Hall itself. Lady Lowden met me at the gates to her south drive and we walked together through meadows of upwards of five hundred young Elvises, stamping and tossing their locks to something called (I think) 'You ain't nothin' but a houn' dock.' The music came from huge loudspeakers hung in the stately park elms. The châtelaine of Dexter Hall smiled and waved beatifically, her ears firmly plugged with screwed up twists of paper from *Country Life*.

'We're doing it for the death-watch beetle, do you see?' my hostess explained. 'I think they're all frightfully good, don't you?'

Of the gyrating youngsters, one or two among the five hundred did bear a passing resemblance to the young man who had entertained me so royally in Spalding those many years ago.

– *Ten* –

A week or so has passed since I last sat down to these pages. The awful and unrelenting pressure of the ordinary and everyday has taken its toll. It has been make and mend in the Jenks camp.

I turned aside from the work under my hand now for a reason – to bring to a head correspondence with Rigton Lane Primary School. The matter is a complicated one and goes back over several years. It concerns, briefly, my offer to deliver a series of lectures to the tots, on subjects of my choosing. Never mind that my services have been tendered free of charge: Mr Cuthbertson, head teacher, has consistently refused my scheme. If I tell you he is the sort of Scotchman who wears a kilt at weekends when mowing his lawns, moreover a person devoted to car rallies and motor sports, you will form some idea of his suitability for the task in which he is employed. Cuthbertson, it goes without saying, is an acquaintance of the Pococks next door. He and Mr Pocock are stalwarts of the snooker room at the village hall. I have no hesitation in describing him as unfit for public office.

'The point is, laddie,' he declared in our most recent telephone conversation, 'while I don't doubt the childhood and early manhood of Marx is a subject you have at your fingertips, I do not believe it would interest a class of six-year-olds on a wet Wednesday afternoon.'

And there I take issue with him, naturally. Marx was a veritable scamp and scallywag as a schoolboy. Some years ago I stumbled across three postcards of Trier, where he was born. They show the Bahnhof, or railway station, the Rathaus, which I presume to be what it says it is – a Rat House and a remarkably fine one – and a view of the Moselle in flood. These could not fail to add vivid illustration to my little talk to the eager-eyed kiddies.

Nor were my other proposals without merit. I mention merely one here: the two-year struggle by Thomas to identify the life cycle of the liver fluke, which work was undertaken in Oxford, 1879–80.

'Great God in Heaven!' Cuthbertson blasphemed, presumably within earshot of his long-suffering secretary, Mrs Pitchford. 'What kind of a contribution to the national curriculum is that, man?'

'The liver fluke,' I replied in my silkiest of tones, 'is one of the more interesting of hermaphrodites, Cuthbertson. It has three larval stages, commencing with its evacuation as an egg from the gut of a sheep or ox. You can picture that easily enough, Headmaster, I suppose. Droppings, to put it plainly. But then the story gathers pace. We can safely describe *Fasciola Hepatica* as a cosmopolitan hermaphrodite because – '

'Get off this line, you pervert,' Cuthbertson shouted.

So be it. Knowledge is never wasted: there will be others who thrill to the idea of the tiny organism attacking the soft parts of the meadow snail with the ferocity of a torpedo. But I keep my powder dry on that one. Meanwhile, I have sent my musings on Marx to the *Cork and Linoleum Gazette*, who some years ago published a squib of mine. It was on accidental electrocution in the home and was cast up in sonnet form (although the last four lines were unfortunately omitted, from pressure of space). They know me well at the *C and L* – they have the cut of my jib, as it were. Cuthbertson is informed of my decision. We shall see who is victor in this battle of the minds.

The head teacher is a curiously effete figure, by the by, the kilt notwithstanding. He has one of those beards that surely takes longer to trim than it takes another man to shave; and he has been seen once or twice at weekends with the further affectation of pink-tinted spectacles. I believe he wishes to indicate an artistic temperament by these ludicrous means: he is widely regarded in the village as an intellectual. Looking at it from the point of view of most villagers, he holds sole licence to that title, for of course it would be their instinctive reaction to stone to death anyone from outside who made such a bold assertion. In the past, he and Marion Pocock have collaborated artistically, she with her rendering of Songs from the Auvergne, he with Lines from Burns. I am told this makes a very queasy evening's entertainment. I note that the pair are careful to restrict their concerts to old folks' homes, where we can suppose the cutting edge of critical comment has, on the whole, been blunted.

However, to return to my story. It is my usual practice to type up my submissions to the great publishing houses of the world on a very serviceable Underwood, once the property of my Beckenham aunt, who passed it on to me in her will. You may imagine my distress when, shortly after firing off 'Naughty Little Karl' to the *Cork and Linoleum*, the trusty old tripe-writer, as Auntie used to call it fondly, suddenly gave up the ghost. The space bar came away in my hand.

At which point, enter Dame Kiri Te Kanawa, the delectable soprano and friend to Royalty, and a Kiwi to be measured alongside Walter 'Duke' Ellington, the father of reversible multi-action chuck lathe gearing, once a passing interest of mine. My meeting with Dame Kiri came about in a most adventitious way. I had decided to make my journey to have the Underwood repaired coincide with a performance by the King's Crouton Morris Men. An announcement in the entertainment section of the local free paper gave it out that the KCMM were to appear at a ceremony inaugurating the new pedestrian precinct, after a blessing of the footpaths etc. by Canon Waterstone, an old adversary of mine. Accordingly, I hied me forth, so to speak, that very Saturday in question.

About the King's Crouton Morris Men, in passing: they are a revivalist folk dance troupe got up by a Mr Potterton, of the firm of Potterton and Newbiggin, Solicitors. King's Crouton lies some fifteen miles distant. The villagers have most unfortunately barred Potterton and his companions from setting foot in the place for what I can only describe as homophobic reasons. The chief obstacle to common sense in King's Crouton is one Tich Wellingfleet, for whom folk tradition is a closed book. Mr Wellingfleet is a scrap metal merchant and plant hire operator with little time for things of the spirit. Accordingly the King's Crouton Men have adopted the name but not in any wise the support of this ancient village.

But be that as it may. I took my ailing tripe-writer – to continue the amusing appellation – to a stationer's in town called Total Office Supplies. Imagine my stark surprise to find as I walked through the door one of the world's most famous songstresses and almost my favourite New Zea-lander in the very act of being harangued by some ill-bred young person called Malcolm.

'You,' this Malcolm was shouting – and I knew he was Malcolm because he wore a name tag to that effect on his lapel – 'you are going to pick up your hat and coat and go! Because I have had it up to here with you, Kiri! A hundred and forty gross of window envelopes is what I call manky ordering. And I don't know that we need thirty dozen underwater marking pens. What is he, this rep, your brother-in-law or something?'

'You rotten beggar,' Kiri cried.

I stepped nimbly between them.

'I will ask you to moderate your language, sir, in front of a Dame of the British Empire and a personal friend of Princess Diana.'

Both Dame Kiri and Malcolm were stunned into silence. I set my Underwood on the counter with a pleasing rattle of its keys.

'Attend to that if you will, young man. Kindly report in writing if the repair is to exceed three pounds. And close you mouth like a good boy. Dame Kiri, may I suggest you fetch your hat and coat? We need detain ourselves here no longer. This is no place for genius.'

'See?' Kiri shouted in triumph. 'I aren't that stupid after all, Mr Clever Clogs Malcolm Branagh.'

And with a toss of those famous raven locks, she pushed the unfortunate Branagh into a display of JottoFax, the personal file system for those with nothing very much to say.

'I'm off to the pub with four-eyes here, and I'll be back for me wages later.'

After which, she blew a loud raspberry. I must say, for someone who was born and raised fourteen thousand miles away in the islands discovered by Captain Cook, she had the local patois off to a tee. Was she perhaps researching for some role in the gloomy but increasingly popular oeuvre of the composer Janáček? Was she (even) engaged in some girlish prank with the wife of the heir to the throne? Several such possibilities raced through my mind. At all events, Dame Kiri pulled on an imitation leather blouson with room in it for any two tenors of her acquaintance and, her dark eyes flashing, left the shop. I hurried after.

'Where d'you wanna go then, Grandad?'

I proposed the tea rooms of the Congregational Church in Flood Street, and she countered with the Drake and Two Ducks, behind the bus station. We were soon ensconced. My mind was buzzing with a hundred ways of breaking the ice. It seemed very small praise indeed to tell her she was the most beautiful Maori ever to sit at a table in the Drake; and in any case she was still clearly much put out. She kicked out with a white fashion boot in the direction of the landlord's large brindled Alsatian, who roamed the tables with a crisp packet snagged between its fangs.

'I suppose,' I began at last, 'the life of the international artiste has its setbacks as well as its glories. It has its miniatures as well as its heroic sweeps.'

'My Uncle Jack was a sweep,' she observed absently. I made a swift note in biro on my wrist, lest I forget the remark.

'And was there much work for him in New Zealand?'

She looked at me with real interest in those liquid eyes of hers.

'Who are you? I mean where do you come from?'

'I am an author and a scholar.'

'Really? What are you writing, just at the mo'?'

'I have just completed a piece on the early years of Marx.'

'Yeah,' Kiri said abstractedly. 'See that man over there, with the swastika tattooed on his forehead? That's Tich Wellingfleet. He's horrible to people.'

I glanced. Wellingfleet was glowering in our direction. A length of lavatory chain hung round his neck. For some reason he was wearing industrial goggles. I would put his weight at about twenty stone. It was a nasty moment.

'D'ja like music?' Dame Kiri asked me from what seemed several thousand miles away.

'I like your music,' I croaked.

'You've heard me then?'

'I am your most devoted fan.'

'Funny. I never seen you up at the club. I'm on tonight, if you fancy it. Bring a pal. I'll bring Jo. She's great for a laugh, she is.'

Dame Kiri Te Kanawa and Miss Josephine Barstow on the same bill in our little market town! I bade my antipodean song thrush farewell and raced as fast as my legs could carry me to Canon Waterstone, whom I knew I could find at the Reading Room of the Central Library at this time of day. It was his habit to call in for a perusal of *World Track and Field*. The reverend sports lover looked up at me with his habitual caution.

'You, Jenks! What insanity has been brewing in you today, you unhappy afflatus?'

'A chance to spend an evening with Dame Kiri Te Kanawa and Miss Josephine Barstow.'

'Is she the one with the girdle of bananas?' Waterstone wanted to know.

'That was Josephine Baker.'

'My father's favourite.'

'Your father was Rural Dean of Chichester,' I remonstrated.

'And a cleric of broad stripe. Though I don't know how much broader you can get than blessing a blessed pedestrian precinct. Which it has been my pleasure to do today. I know where I'd rather seek out the Christian message. This Dame Kiri gal – is she the one with the pretty face?'

'The face, the voice, the gestures and the accents of an angel.'

'Good heavens, Jenks,' Waterstone scoffed. 'I haven't seen you in this state of elevation since that ghastly Wivens woman undertook to teach you to swim. Get a grip on yourself, man.'

'You, Waterstone,' I replied with feeling, 'have consistently represented yourself to me as a man of the arts. I understand your sermons abound with a call to honour the spiritual side of man's make-up. By great good chance, I have discovered one of the world's greatest sopranos to be here, in a fashion of speaking, on your ecclesiastical doorstep – and what do I get from you? Contumely.'

'What time does this thing kick off?' he wanted to know.

How pleasant to report, therefore, that Waterstone and I enjoyed an evening of coloratura. But we reckon without the accidental strokes of fate at our peril. As we sauntered arm in arm up the shopping precinct – for Waterstone has a Johnsonian side to him – a most terrible situation was revealed. The King's Crouton Morris Men had fallen foul of the Leeds United Hard Team. This, I fancy, requires fuller explanation.

The Hard Team are youths, some thirty in number, who support a football club called, apparently, Leeds United. That explains sufficiently the first part of their title. Their reputation for unruliness is legendary and I am told we would have to plunder the annals of the Mongols under Genghis Khan to find apt parallel for their astonishing want of human mercy. It transpires that British Rail have hit on the device of transporting them to away matches in closed trains, rather similar to that which took Lenin on his fateful journey from Zurich to the Finland Station, St Petersburg.

But British Rail have added a refinement, not, as far as I know, contemplated by the German High Command in 1917. The Hard Team are persuaded on to the train at Leeds with free lager and (some say) raw meat. They are taken to any town yet to experience their bluff ways. They are then tricked into debouching from the train by tapes made for the railway by well-known radio actors, giving cries of, for example, 'C'mon you Reds!' or 'Liver-poo'!' Thus it was on this particular Saturday, the lads, supposing themselves to be on the way to attending a match at the Dell, home of Southampton FC, found themselves instead in a newly consecrated pedestrian precinct, face to face with a jigging group of middle-aged men in unpressed cricket trousers, with ribbons round their hats.

Their indignation was awesome to behold. Within minutes, £17,000 of damage had been caused and the Team were busy uprooting an equestrian statue of the Prince Consort that stands at the head of the new precinct. Shoppers fled in all directions. The police were hemmed into the doorway of Panti-Box, a specialist in ladies' underwear, from which they attempted fruitless sallies.

Your question is clear. How did these events

come to bear on the concert given by Dame Kiri and her illustrious coeval, Miss Josephine Barstow? The answer lies in the eccentric but fearless character of Austin Waterstone. Seeing a shaven-skulled sportsman tearing at a litter bin with his bare teeth, Waterstone let out the single piercing cry: 'Julian!'

The youth paused in his mawing, and stared at us incredulously. Then came a dawning recognition.

'I say! Canon Water-Wally!'

'Call off your unruly pack of dogs this instant, Julian. Be done, I command you in the name of God!' Waterstone cried.

'Crumbs! To pitch up here – my home town – I can't believe it! You're going to think me the most awful twink, Austers, but it is so terribly dull at the Uni. The Music Department's really naff socially and I'm not even sure I want to play the fiddle any more. I'm really into mindless violence these days.'

Thus Julian Beamish, the son of a perfectly respectable optician in the town and one-time chorister of St Chad's. Waterstone, with no thought of his own safety, strode to the youth and clouted him over the ear with a bulging shopping bag. He was felled by (especially) four tins of catfood. Austin Waterstone was as a figure from the Old Testament in his righteous anger.

'Enough, I say! This is not the way of a Chad. End this rumble this instant. And take that safety pin out of your nostril, you young fool.'

'I hate the University of Leeds,' the peculiar Beamish shrilled. 'I want to be a thug!'

'My, how you've changed since you and I sat reading Housman together,' Waterstone breathed. 'Have you forgotten so soon, Moony-Boops?'

The boy burst into tears.

We fetched up with the rest of the Hard Team at the Duck and Two Drakes, where we found Tich Wellingfleet pinned to the wall by steak knives. Here we met Julian's dearest pal, Snot, who had eaten the lad's fiddle at the beginning of his second year and thus cut him off from a life of music. Beamish was blubbering uncontrollably. In my opinion he has more than a little to live down with his peer group. Snot passed me a pint of Old Predictable.

'Get that down you, son,' he said.

'Help yourselves, lads,' the landlord cried like the ghost of Hamlet's father, from under our feet. He and his wife had taken refuge in the cellars. There began an afternoon of incredible drinking.

The Hard Team voted our little community the nicest they had visited in a long while. Their trophies were many and various, ranging from King's Crouton hats to consumer items like video recorders. At four-forty in the afternoon the football results were closely attended by those still able to see and hear – and since Chelsea and Millwall lost that day, the mood of well-being was extended into the early evening.

It was Snot's idea that we should go on to the Te Kanawa-Barstow concert. Taking with us pieces of pub furniture as souvenirs, we made our way to the venue, a modest concrete hut on the Robert Boothby estate. I confess I was as elated as the next man.

But there my ignominy began. Snot explained the laws of mobhandedness to me as we gathered in front of the entrance, barred from entering by lads not unsimilar to the Hard Team, but with the advantage of being sober. Taunts and milk bottles flew. The plan was that one of us should effect an entrance through any open window, and then admit the rest through the emergency doors.

The only available window was that giving ventilation to the ladies' toilet and it was I, *nolens volens*, who was boosted halfway through. Halfway, as Julian commiserated later, to Paradise. By the most miserable mischance, who should be occupying the facilities but one whom I least intended to offend. Dame Kiri's scream ran through three octaves.

Nothing it seems, no telephone call of mine, nor effusion of my pen, can erase that awful moment. Even my card of condolence c/o The Royal Opera House has been returned to me. Scrawled across the brief verse is the suggestion I should see a doctor. Dear Dame, I was trying to see an opera.

– *Eleven* –

The careful reader will recall that my mother ran off with Gerald Smight, Schools Attendance Officer, in the spring of 1944. The erring couple made their way to Arbroath, there to confess their passion to Gerald's wife Annie, who was in the process of opening a fish and chip shop in Skate Street. I have made promise to touch on their later history, the details of which came to hand in a most curious way. I believe the story may be of interest. It has a pleasant curlicue.

Some while ago I loaned Canon Austin Waterstone the manuscript copy of my novel based upon the life of Bishop Adalbert. It was at the beginning of our acquaintanceship and I had yet to detect the levity that has surely held Waterstone back from high office. It was then his habit to invite his cronies round on Thursday evenings to something that came to be called the Cavils Club. Leading Cavillers were Bryon Portmadoc, a baton-wielder with the Salzburg Sinfonietta, the oddly named group he founded of local peripatetic music teachers and what we must call, in charity, other string players; Ken Noad, firebrand but unfortunately tyro television playwright; and the poet and proprietor of *Slash*, Mitchell Dunstable. My purpose in submitting Adalbert to the Cavils Club was obvious enough: I had been led to believe by Waterstone that I could be admitted to membership if, as he put it, the thing came anywhere near up to snuff.

It did not. At that time in the history of the Club, Portmadoc was setting new standards of pettifogging objectionableness. His marriage had recently foundered; a Trio for Tuba, Flute and Viola had been returned from Bulgaria with an insulting letter in the language of that country; and eczema had taken toll of the musician's features. I was blackballed; and nothing Waterstone could do was to reverse the decision.

'A bitter shame, a bitter shame,' he commiserated. 'Portmadoc is up for Faultfinder-General next year, and there's little we can do to stop him.'

'I thought Mitchell Dunstable was Faultfinder-General Elect.'

'That versifying idiot,' Waterstone exclaimed, true as ever to the traditions of the Club. 'Here's your manuscript back, old lad, with no hard feelings. Oh, and by the way, there's a postcard tucked in there somewhere. I'd no idea you ever lived in Penang. Must tell me about it some time.'

My association with the *Penang Telegraph & Argus* came about quite fortuitously. The editor of this small but well-respected newspaper was for many years one M. J. Sockalingam. We met by chance in the lifts at Covent Garden Tube station, I on my way to the stage door of the Royal Opera House, he to dinner with a Fleet Street friend. To cut a long story short, there was a power failure, the lifts jammed, and M.J. and I found ourselves thrown together for some three hours of total darkness. I learned a great deal about Malaysia's trade in tin; and fancy I gave back something in return of our own island heritage. Sockalingam was a man small in stature but with a huge heart. Once he had mastered the structure of 'Ten Green Bottles' he would sing nothing else, and so we sat on the floor, making the best of it, brothers in adversity. We were released by firemen shortly after midnight.

For two years subsequently I sent M.J. a weekly column for his feature pages, which he published in Malay under the cross-heading 'Notes and Jottings from Abroad'. Happening to have to hand a working copy of Winstedt's *Malay Grammar* and the same author's enchanting *Dictionary of Colloquial Malay*, I was able to retranslate my pieces and from time to time a lively correspondence flowed from that. For example, for some months, although the cross-head remained, 'Notes and Jottings' actually contained spot prices for Burmese smelting tin, a very amusing transposition of copy. But our personal friendship never faltered. I soon gained enough proficiency in Malay to write my friend lengthy letters, to which he replied at more leisurely intervals on sometimes rather scandalous postcards.

I have no idea how a copy of the *Penang Telegraph* made its way to Scotland, but in 1972 I was astonished to find in the post a picture postcard depicting the Electric Glen in Ayrshire. This had been sent to the *T&A* by sea mail, the Queen's Head machin torn from some vending machine set in the wall of the Arbroath GPO franked by Paquebot cancel, Penang; incurring the 12c reddish violet postage due stamp on arrival; readdressed with the addition of the rather vulgar 50c multicoloured commemorative of 1969, depicting Tunku Abdul Rahman; somehow finding its way back to me with the further box cachet in blue, 'Damaged by Snails'. An interesting and valuable piece of postal history in its own right, but what electrified me was the superscription, which I quote in full: *Dearest Claude, How do you find the heat? Yours ever, G. S. Smight*. A rapid calculation showed that Smight was now ninety if he was a day: nor had we met or corresponded since he disappeared with my mother in 1944. But in some fashion only to be guessed at, he had noticed my by-line in the *Telegraph* and acted upon it in this somewhat casual way. After only a little reflection, I put my immediate affairs in order and oiled the Rudge. It was stark winter, and the journey up the A1 was tedious in the extreme, but I was spurred on by curiosity. What would I find in Arbroath, if that is where he was?

My mother is buried in the St Andrew's Kirk, alongside her rival and friend Annie Smight. The Brothock runs close by. It is as peaceful a resting place as you could wish. The headstones do not reveal the true story of these two women, nor I suppose is there any way in which they could. They died within a year of each other, leaving Gerald Smight to soldier on alone. This he had done with some success, for when I met him he was driving a Ford Anglia and playing social golf twice a week. I would not have recognised him, in all honesty, had it not been for the faint squeaking of his tin leg as we sat in the mixed lounge of the Club, gazing out over the snow-covered 18th green.

'We meant to write, old CJ,' he murmured. 'But in any case you were away to Penang. Hot out there, I should imagine. I've seen pictures of the girls. Fine, well set-up young women. You did the right thing, doubtless. You did the right thing.'

Gerald Smight was simply very old. He was quite the oldest man I had ever met, and the years had melted away his anxiety, his moustache-chewing uncertainty. In its place was a smiling serenity. Time – and the attentions of two women – had served him well. I quickly learned to cope with the holes that riddled his memory like a chunk of Jahlsberg cheese.

'How is Sandy?' he asked suddenly.

'Fine. Sandy is fine, Uncle Gerald.'

'A terrible thing, to lose your swing. Does he still have the little dog?'

'I believe that died,' I said, wondering how to manage the rest of my visit. Gerald studied me thoughtfully.

'Winnie's gone, you know.'

'Has she?'

'I never liked him. A warmonger.'

And so on. But after a tea of gammon and eggs he perked up considerably and drove me at ten miles an hour to the family home, a bungalow overlooking the sea. He parked the car on the lawn and ushered me inside.

'Your mother'll be in soon,' he said with heart-rending gentleness.

'This is a fine bungalow, Uncle Gerald.'

He looked about him as if seeing it for the first time.

'Of its kind, Claude. Of its kind. Have we had Christmas, can you tell me?'

I pieced together their story little by little. Annie Smight and my mother were cut from the same cloth – urgent, hyperactive, ambitious. The fish and chip shop in Skate Street was soon the focal centre of Arbroath night life. A huge tile mural depicted a man in yellow oilskins hauling in a catch of cod that would have done justice to the Galilean. The stainless steel of the apparatus was polished a refulgent silver. Annie's, as the shop was called, was the first of its kind to introduce the mushy pea to Scotland, or so claimed the fond Gerald. On Saturday nights, a piper played 'Crimond' and other tunes of that ilk to entertain the queue.

'We *were* somebody, Claude. The three of us together *were* somebody. The folk came for their wedding photographs beside Big Willie hauling in the cod. When it was time, they brought their babies in to see us.'

'And what was your role, Uncle Gerald?'

'Master of the house,' he sniggered.

The three of them retired in 1960. Annie and my mother took up bowls, Gerald joined the golf club.

'The Three Musketeers, son. You were in Penang. So be it. We muddled along. In fact I got down to seven quite quickly. You're hitting against that leg anyway, Claude, do you get my drift? That's the secret of the swing, a braced right leg. Well, I had an advantage. Apart from corrosion, from the salt air, the tin leg did me proud. And still does.'

He still smoked a pipe, also, at colossal risk to himself and the fabric of the bungalow. We talked through a haze of burning wool and the more toxic gases released from his armchair cushions. I extinguished him as tactfully as I could whenever he burst into actual flame. The old fellow rambled contentedly the while.

'Jack Morrissey passed over a fortnight ago.'

'I'm sorry to hear that.'

'I didn't see it, but the plane passed right over the house, apparently. You may have come across his daughter. Moira.'

'The name doesn't ring a bell.'

'I wouldn't give a thank you for Oslo,' he said moodily.

'Is that where Moira lives?'

'She lives in Canada. Oslo is where Jack was headed.'

And so on. I will not weary you with Gerald's fitful grasp upon the here and now or, as it was, the there and then. We watched television, at his insistence. Horses with improbable names jumped over obstacles seldom to be met with on any planet where equestrianism has value. Uncle Gerald seemed to know a great deal about it.

'Ho! look at that,' he cackled, as some fool scattered wooden bricks in all directions. 'Now it's up to the plucky Irishman.'

Later, he asked me many a sly question about Penang. For him, all Asiatics were the same – and since the town had just greeted its first family of Hong Kong Chinese, he appeared to confuse north-west Malaysia with south-east China, at any rate in respect of their womenfolk.

'The Mandarin, they call their place. The chips are nothing, your mother would have something to say about the chips – but there's a lassie there who takes the orders – '

He fell out of his chair with nonegenarian enthusiasm.

None of which would be of the slightest interest, were it not that by these means I met Uncle Gerald's golf partner. Like many another old man before him, Uncle tended to conceptualise a golf club as a sort of non-residential hotel, and accordingly we set off there in the morning, shortly after nine. Once again our progress was painfully slow and erratic, not helped in the slightest by blizzard conditions. For half a mile or more we drove along the beach, while the fuses snapped and fizzed in his memory and he kept up a constant stream of *non sequiturs*. How he had managed to keep his licence even in such a tolerant community as Arbroath was a mystery. However, we came to rest at last on the practice putting green and Uncle was carried in pig-a-back by the steward's wife.

'This is Claude, Molly,' he shouted through the driving snow. 'From Penang, where the weather's a bit more clement. Is Bing in yet?'

'So he is, Mr Smight, so he is, and a bonny sight withal.'

'Let's hope the snow stays for Christmas, Molly.'

'That would be a fine thing, sir, it would indeed.'

It was of course the second week in March. The

good woman staggered up the thirty-nine steps to the clubhouse.

'A White Christmas, eh? Bing's favourite song.'

'Mebbe not his favourite exactly, would you say, Mr Smight? But it has made the man powerfully full in the pocket, no doubt about that.'

Like you, I hardly expected to see Bing Crosby actually present in the clubhouse, any more than I supposed the halls would be decked with boughs of holly. However, as we entered the cards room of the splendid old building, there was Bing as large as life, relaxed and puffing on an unfilled pipe, in between bouts of very liquid whistling of the song that is *not* called 'In the Bub-Bub-Blue of the Night'. He greeted us in that familiar baritone voice, at once friendly and sardonic.

'Poor day for a round of golf, Claude,' he smiled.

'From Penang.' (This from Uncle Gerald.)

'A long way to come.'

'I'm very happy to meet you, sir.'

'And I to meet you, my friend. Pull up a pew, *relaxez-vous*.'

And here I interject what seems to be a most necessary emphasis: there did still exist in me for a few more minutes or so the doubt that this pleasant fellow was indeed Bing Crosby. I say this, because in the informal telling of this story on previous occasions, scorn has been poured and eyebrows raised. It has been suggested, for example, that Bing was not Bing but 'Bing', some genial golfing pensioner and five-day member mistaken by my Uncle for the genuine article. Out of kindness for the old fellow, the central argument runs, this 'Bing' impersonated the singer, though being in fact – let us say – a retired fruiterer, or pensioned-off civil servant. I have had a dozen practical objections raised to the notion that the man sitting before me was the crooner. To all my doubters – and to you – I have but one word. The word is ears. Crosby noticed me looking at them.

'Something got you by the collar there, Claude old boy?'

'I was just looking at your ears, Mr Crosby.'

'Only two I have. One on each side, same as all the other fellows.'

His pleasant blue eyes searched mine. I leaned forward.

'Your secret is safe with me, sir,' I muttered.

'Always good to hear, old Claude. What secret is that, exactly?'

'The ears have convinced me.'

'The ears have simply rolled away, my friend.'

'Not those ears,' I smiled. 'Never.'

Bing looked a little confused for a second, as though we were at cross purposes.

'Excuse me,' I muttered. 'Did you say ears or years?'

'What are you two young devils whispering about?' Uncle Gerald demanded, attempting to sit in his chair, and falling on the floor with a clatter of tin like a teatray dropped from an upstairs window.

'Gerald,' Bing said to the heap on the floor, 'I think what we have here in this boy is a chip off the old block.'

'I just wish my mother and Auntie Elsie could see us talking like this. Auntie Elsie was especially fond of you. And of course it would make my mother's day.'

Uncle Gerald looked at me with a rare flash of sanity. 'I thought I explained, CJ. Your mother passed over some years hence. Wasn't it you I took to the church to see her? Or was that someone else? Or did I go alone?'

'Let's play pinochle,' Bing suggested diplomatically.

What Crosby was doing there, how long he had been a member at Arbroath, how he had time or patience to play this undemanding game with a ninety-year-old child of three, I do not know. Today, I regard the encounter I had with Bing from a selfish point of view. Had poor Gerald Smight ended his days in pleasant bickering with Konrad Adenauer, or Bertrand Russell, or anyone else, it would have been just as enjoyable for him, doubtless. Crosby lent to Arbroath and the story of the Smights and my mother a strange and faintly maudlin redolence. I was quite right: she would have been delighted to hear him joshing Gerald in his inimitable style. After watching them play cards for some while, I joined the club steward at the bar.

'Twa canny wee goffers,' this craggy servant observed fondly. 'An' each yin as daft as the other, if you take my meaning. The wifey was saying the bald one's your Uncle Gerald.'

'A true *cavaliere servante* and a friend of my mother's.'

'Is that a fact?'

Uncle Gerald, like Bing, died on the golf course. He went into the fairway bunker at the par five fourth and when after half an hour he had not come out, his playing partners summoned the greens staff to have him removed. There was a modest funeral which I was unable to attend, not having been invited. By one of those twists of fate that supply novel writers with their plots, Bing died the same day, in Spain. I wrote to Arbroath, in case the old man had missed the news. He had, of course. After a month or so, I received a parcel from the captain of the club, an Archie MacIver. It contained the tin leg that had set my mother's heart on fire all those many years ago. Perhaps as a mark of honour from the fellows at the club, or perhaps through an oversight, it wore a spiked golf shoe. I will simply say this: I took that leg to the woods where once we had lived in the tar-paper shack, and left it leaning against a beech tree. It seemed a fitting thing to do.

– *Twelve* –

Last year, I spent some weeks looking for a thirty-inch bicycle wheel with the old Sturmey Archer gear. In the current jargon, it was an away-from-base operation and my enquiries led me at last to call in at a stamp shop in Stourbridge for directions.

I describe the place I entered as a stamp shop, but a sorry excuse for such it was. As it happens, philately and I are lifelong chums. I well remember meeting Beecham, in the last years of his illustrious life, at a beach hut in Chapel St Leonards, on the Lincolnshire coast between Skegness and Mable-thorpe. The conductor was sitting on the verandah to Sunnyside with a rug over his knees. He at first vehemently denied that he was the matchless inter-preter of Mozart I knew him to be. The founder of the Philharmonic waved me away, though I would not be gainsaid. I happened to notice that on his lap were some pages of Venezuelan stamps issued for the State of Guyana.

'Your special favourites, Sir Thomas!'

'Worth a mint,' he muttered gruffly.

'Indeed, if genuine. Hand-stamped with the blue control to be sure, but, unless I miss my mark, reprinted from the original plates on different coloured papers. And thus, honoured sir, likely to fall into the category of forgery.'

I was of course gleaning this information from an upside down reading of the stamps at a metre or more – and in the teeth of a stiff onshore breeze. Sand whipped up from the beach was stinging our faces. Beecham peered at the open pages of his album and then looked up at me with a strange, almost a pitiable expression.

'Take them,' he said, in a choked voice. 'Take the stamps. I don't know who you are, or how you found me here, but take the damn things and go.'

'Only if you will do me the honour first of appending your signature. Were you to add: "To my friend Claude Jenks" . . .'

Instead, he rose from his chair with a half-sob and withdrew into the tiny interior of Sunnyside, closing the door behind him. I heard nothing more, save the melancholy opening strains of 'A Walk in the Paradise Gardens,' played on a wind-up gramophone.

'And did,' I asked the proprietor of the Stour-bridge Stamp Bazaar now, after recounting this little anecdote, 'did the great old baton-wielder ever bend his steps this way, I wonder? Did you have dealings with him, as might easily have been the case?'

'The most famous bloke we ever had in here was Frank Sinatra,' Monsieur Le Timbre said with the smirk the stupid reserve for wit. Not for the first time, I found how taxing it is to deal with the provincial humorist. I refused to rise to the bait, and instead pressed him hard on the Sturmey Archer problem, with which you will remember I had entered the shop.

'Jeffrey yes, Sturmey no,' this wag bantered with me. 'This, my old mate, is a stamp shop, not a bike factory.'

At that moment, in through the door came President Kenneth Kaunda! He was without his fly-whisk, but wore a linen safari suit under a dark blue nylon anorak. On his head was a wool hat knitted in the colours of West Bromwich Albion. I alone recognised him and gave him an immediate and enthusiastic *salaam*, *Effendi*.

'*Hamjambo?*' I enquired. '*Habari gani ya siku mingi?*'

He seemed – if it does not seem boastful – he seemed astonished to be addressed thus. His reply was in English and very much to the point. He was in the shop to ask directions to the bus station. He must needs be in Hereford by nightfall.

I instantly invited him to a pot of tea at the Linga Longa Café, which happened to be next door, and bidding our farewells to the astonished philatelist, we exchanged the cathedral quiet of the Stamp Bazaar for the hurly-burly of the Linga Longa.

Kaunda ordered egg and chips, explaining in excellent idiomatic English that he was feeling gutted from a late night at some sort of reception in Birmingham.

'But where,' I asked, 'is your retinue? Where your advisers and *chefs de cabinet*? Or are you, on this occasion, like Coeur de Lion, travelling about the kingdom incognito?'

'Summat like that,' he acknowledged, after a moment or two. I felt pressed to engage him in as much local history as I could muster, and talked as well as I could on the discovery of the famous Stourbridge fire-clay by wandering Frenchmen in 1557. I fear I may have strayed from that to the rival merits of the sun-and-planet gearing and the so-called Derailleur variable gear, giving preference to the sturdy English system. Kaunda laid his head on the table.

'You know what Shit Creek is, don't you, pal?' he asked in an imploring voice. Certain banking arrangements having fallen through at the last moment, he found himself strapped for cash, but with an imperative need to get down to Hereford.

'A light bulb is switched on in my head, *Effendi!*'

'You got the message, eh?'

'You are going,' I divined, 'to the Three Choirs Festival!'

Now this realisation was of importance, for I have a great affection for the Three Choirs. Within the family there is a strong Elgarian connection. It is not generally known that for five years from 1879 Elgar held the post of conductor-composer at the County Lunatic Asylum in his native Worcestershire. My great-grandfather, on my father's side, was, so to speak, bassoonist-in-residence at the time. While no hard documentary evidence exists, I have often thought of the young Elgar sharing a joke and impressions of life with that distant Jenks, whose bottom C was never, sadly, recorded. I told Kaunda of this and he raised his head from the table at last.

'And you are descended from this same bloke? I'm getting a picture. What was you saying about the sturdy old Sturmey Archer? Pay up here, and I think your probs are over. You get me down to Hereford and I will oblige. I will get you a choice of the little devils.'

'President *Effendi*,' I began, filled with emotion.

'You can call me Ken,' he muttered. 'But let's get across to the Lamb and Flag now, there's a good lad.'

We left on the last bus out of Stourbridge. And a very roistering crowd we were. A party of darts players on their way home to Ledbury had been engaged in a challenge match against the Combined Clergy of Walsall, who stepped up to the ockie under their *nom de guerre*, the Ecumenicals. The clergy had smitten the ungodly hip and thigh. I had this of a dark-eyed Ledburian, who explained that the vicars had been scoring in hymn numbers. By the way he laid his finger against his nose, I saw there had also been malfeasance.

'It ended in a bit of a punch-up,' my informant admitted. Matters had only been resolved by the intervention of the Bishop himself, Nine Dart Teddy Partington, who volunteered drinks all round and a lift at least as far as Stourbridge, with an initial detour to Walsall General, where a Congregational Minister had the winner's trophy removed from his throat.

Kaunda, as befitted his station in life, gave some sign of reprehending all this. He took no part in the badinage, but lay in the aisle of the bus with my haversack for pillow. We parted at the bus depot, with an arrangement to meet the following morning.

'Don't forget now,' the President begged me, my hand firmly gripped in his. 'Don't you let the old Pres' down, you hear?'

This last he repeated several times, as watched by amused police, smoking – against all regulations – in their patrol car, we parted company at last. My own steps led me to call upon a couple I had met by chance in 1974, while mapping a population of willow-warblers in Waltham Forest.

'You did mention,' I reminded the distaff side of the household through the letter-box, 'that if ever I were to find myself in Hereford I should look you up.'

'But it's gone one in the morning,' the lady complained.

'And very frosty withal.'

After a welcome plate of beans on toast, I turned in, making the best use I could of the couch and an armful of blankets. My hosts had excused themselves some time earlier. I could hear raised voices in the bedroom above me. Towards three, the man of the house went on some errand in his car, I have no idea where. The slam of his front door was like a pistol shot, and since I had been dreaming of Kaunda and the risks attaching to political life in the one-party democracies of Africa, I stumbled to my feet, lashing about me blindly, and in the process knocking over a collection of Goss china.

The President and I met as planned next morning on the steps of the cathedral. Kaunda was in more jovial mood altogether. There was an addition to his wardrobe. On his feet he wore faded red bedroom slippers with nylon fur edging. In his hand was a cooling bag of bacon sandwiches. I proposed we took early seats for the Hattersley 'Missa Solemnis' for choir and gamelan orchestra, to be given its world premiere that morning. Kaunda countered with a suggestion that we walk out to a friend of his who could assist with the Sturmey Archer.

'Or my name's not Ken Kaunda,' he quipped gaily.

'But the Hattersley is a first performance,' I objected.

Needs must we leave the glories of the cathedral and the gathering crowd of Hattersley lovers, who now numbered some fifteen or more, and set out for an estate of council houses in a far part of the town. The President declared his footwear excellent for level walking in dry conditions. He was, he said, a man who knew shoes. On the way he pointed out many other things of interest – as for example the many cross-breeds of dog to be got when one or two alsatians are let loose in a sector of public housing. We arrived at last at Dalton Avenue and picked our way to Number 47.

There being no answer to our knocking – apart from a ferocious barking – we made our way to the back of the house, past a commercial van propped up at each axle end with housebricks. Kaunda hollooed. To my delight and astonishment, a frail white-haired old man came from a garden shed. He wore a donkey jacket and walked with the aid of a stick, and though his hand shaded his face in an attitude of suspicion, I recognised him instantly.

'You,' I cried, 'are Michael Foot!'

The Sturmey Archer hub gear may seem to the younger element to have been superseded. The call these days is for mountain bikes, sold in more quantities than would be justified in Tibet, and certainly in excess of the number of mountains to be found in and about central London. Michael Foot and President Kaunda are each of a generation to grasp the difference between bicycling and the new business. We sat on a rickety bench and shared our reprehensions. The distinguished biographer, political essayist and Member of Parliament asked me whether the gear was for my own use.

'By no means. I am upon this quest for a correspondent, a retired midwife from New Cumnock.'

'And is that where you want the thing to end up?' Kaunda asked.

The two political giants exchanged smiling glances.

'Had you said Old Cumnock,' Foot said, 'I should have been stumped, I tell you that quite frankly. But New Cumnock is known to me as no other place in Scotland, for it is there I once contemplated opening a car battery business, isn't that right, Ken?'

'You were going to open a car battery business,' Kaunda confirmed.

'And lucky for you, Claude,' Foot continued, 'my connections with that leafy show-town of Ayrshire are good to this day. My sister's boy Duane will run your Sturmey Archer up the road for you this very weekend.'

And so might have concluded a pleasant and revealing morning. But there now hove into view an X-registered Cavalier, driven by a large man in a vest, torn tweed trousers and unlaced tennis shoes.

He jumped from the car, kicked away some marauding dogs and pointed a dramatic finger at President Kaunda.

'Yes,' he bellowed, 'I've been looking for you, sunshine. Oh yes. I may look stupid, but you are for the chop. Oh yes!'

To my utter astonishment, my friend the President of Zambia not only did not contradict this boor, but stayed not upon the order of his going, so to speak, and went. He leaped a low wire fence into the neighbour's and set off at a crouching run through a bed of cabbage. One or two were kicked up like dewy footballs in his flight.

'My dear man – '

I was of course going to tell him what you already know, of the importance of those whom he was addressing.

'I don't know *you*,' Mr Dirty Vest cried. 'But you are just my boxing weight, sunshine.'

And picking me up by a leg, he flung me by main force on to the roof of Michael Foot's garage.

I tried to make the hospital understand, but in vain. A little after two in the afternoon, a perfectly miniature Singhalese came and spoke to me in broken English. After some difficulties, I accepted he might be what he claimed to be, and that was a doctor.

'Hullo?' he bellowed in my ear. 'Yes please? How

many fingers do I hold up? What is all this nonsense about President of Zambia? You are taking drugs, stimulants? What is the name of the Prime Minister?'

The policeman who was waiting for me in casualty was young and bored. He surprised me twice in conversation, once by announcing that he was married and had a baby called Kimberley. The other remark was potentially more interesting – he expressed an absolute passion for Schopenhauer. But my pleasure was short-lived. He seemed to think he was describing someone who pulled on a Number 8 shirt for Borussia Dortmund.

– *Thirteen* –

Poems from Ursula. She came round last night to browse the shelves as she put it. She took away with her Milton, a translation of Ovid and F. R. Leavis's *The Great Tradition*. Heaven knows what she will fashion from these. I asked if she had ever read any Stevie Smith.

'Is he the one with the red hair that keeps winning all the time?' she asked, baffling me completely.

However, I was able to show her my newest acquisition, a postcard signed by Adolf Gollmick, whom you will recall was born in Frankfurt and settled in London in 1844. He is best known as the founder of the Kilburn Musical Association and composer of the dramatic cantata 'The Blind Beggar of Bethnal Green'. His postcard is addressed to a Miss Ethel Buckingham at an address in Peckham and shows a picture of the front at Worthing. It reads 'Weather fine. Kippers for breakfast. Has

Amy had the baby yet?' An important addition to Gollmick studies, I do not doubt.

Ursula can be quite endearing. Her poetry would put a rhinoceros to sleep but she tries hard to interest herself in things of the mind and, as she has pointed out, was hardly required to count past five during her time with Dr Stanley Wivens. In fact we had a pleasant evening of it, sorting postcards, dusting fossils and the like. She is somewhat of a faddist in matters of food, and we ate a working supper of a dish called veggie-burger, made to her own recipe. In taste, it is rather like a pakora that has been irradiated by gamma rays to render it inert.

The question is not what it tastes like, but how it will be considered – what sort of a job-sheet it will get – once it has been ingested. Ursula has a vivid and totally inaccurate picture of the workings of the human body and seems especially fascinated by enzymes. She described them to me as like little men in different coloured overalls who eat at the same canteen but do completely different work.

'They live in your tummy, Claude. Here.'

She lifted up her sweater and pointed to her own stomach. I quickly passed her a box-file of Guatamalan overprints and suggested she cross-catalogue them. I knew only too well that Mrs Strutt was standing on a stepladder a floor below us, a pint beer glass pressed to the ceiling.

★

It was the poet W. H. Auden who first put into my head the idea that my occasional meetings with the famous might be of interest to a wider audience. I ran across him once at Skipton Cattle Market. It was most certainly an unusual place for us to have met. Even after refurbishments that are the pride of all Airedale, there is a rough-edged hurly-burly to the Cattle Market, a sort of busy rural hugger-mugger that would seem at first blush the last place to stumble over an international sophisticate like Wystan. Nor was he dressed the part of the poet. It being a raw day in February, he wore a Bundeswehr greatcoat and was shod in short white surgical boots. On his head he sported a chequered 'Dalesman' cap with a plastic rose tucked into the neb. There are many who would have passed him by with but a single glance. I recognised him instantly.

It may be of interest to my reader to learn what I was doing in the Gateway to the Dales. This is a most engaging story in its own right and while it draws us away from poetry for a moment, there is in it a human dimension that is well worthy of inclusion here. Accordingly, just for the moment, let us leave Auden leaning on the boards that surround the auction ring, a sardonic presence wreathed in the breath of cattle, the clatter of hooves in his ear.

I was once fortunate enough to make the acquaintance of the Chief Justice of Nigeria, shortly after the independence of that country in 1959. In fact, I was of material assistance to him in a pressing problem of personal finance. The Chief Justice approached me in, of all places, the Frinton Public Library, where I was doing some research on the Frinton Martyrs, less celebrated than they should be in that pleasant Essex resort. He shook hands and came immediately and persuasively to the point – he was recalled to Nigeria, found himself temporarily strapped for cash, was trying to raise the fare to London, where the Embassy could be of assistance, but would welcome meanwhile a small loan, secured by a promise to repay issued on the authority of the Executive Council of Nigeria.

I was happy to oblige him, and we walked to the station together. He was, I don't quite know how or why, a popular figure in Frinton, and waved heartily to friends on bicycles and the like. He urged me not to wait with him for the train but to resume my seat at the library. We shook hands again and bade each other farewell.

Well and good. Now it happened that I was in correspondence at that time with another scholar – a considerable amateur of local history and great Yorkshireman – Dr Karl-Otto Wallfisch. Dr Wallfisch and I exchanged regular letters on matters of mutual interest for several years. From time to time we made postal borrowings from each other's libraries. Some months after assisting the Chief Justice of Nigeria to a single fare from Frinton to London, I had need to recoup my outlay by applying to the

Executive Council, as agreed between the parties. But I could not find the promissory note, which was quite small, having been torn from the pages of a racing diary.

It occurred to me that I might have left the paper as a bookmark in Dr Wallfisch's intriguing monograph 'Field Stones of Lower Littondale'. Now the reader begins to see, as it were, the train approaching. I wrote to Dr Wallfisch, he checked in his library; the paper was there; the matter resolved. He enclosed it with Seasonal Greetings, in the shape of a hand-made card, showing his wife Audrey sitting on a Wallfisch field stone near the village of Heyup.

Poor Wallfisch! Before Twelfth Night was out he was laid to rest beneath the frozen earth in his beloved Dale. On Boxing Day of that year it snowed heavily in Pennine Yorkshire, and the good doctor got out his skis for a spin down the valley side. His glasses frosting over in the intense cold, he ran full-tilt into an unmapped field stone some eleven feet high and weighing over a ton and a quarter. Burly though the genial Austrian was, it proved no contest and he was dashed to pieces in the twinkling of an eye. Police estimate that he was travelling in excess of forty miles per hour when he hit the obstacle.

Just a little further, and we can rejoin Auden, who waits patiently at Skipton Cattle Mart. Audrey Wallfisch was doubtless a fine woman, but I always felt no true helpmeet to K-O. There was a streak of hysteria in her that he had sometimes mentioned, though guardedly, in our friendly letters. Nevertheless, you may imagine my surprise when, hardly a month after her husband's death, I received a letter couched in the most abusive terms, accusing me of stealing from what was now his estate Vol. 24 of the *Denkschrift der Schweizerischen Naturforchenden Gesellschaft*; and demanding its return. The only response an Englishman should ever make to such an accusation is dignified silence. And this I did. But in short order I received a letter from a firm of solicitors in Skipton, Messrs Binnie, Blakeson and Wakelam, repeating the charge. It was this business that brought me to Skipton. I was on my way to this trio of lawyers when, taking a wrong turn by the canal, I found myself face to face with Auden.

He was at first studiously non-commital. It was of course market day and a little earlier a Friesian bull had broken loose. Eschewing the obvious attractions of a china shop it had plunged instead into W. H. Smith's. The poor creature, pausing only to vent its bowels, had escaped by leaping through the rear window of the store and was now at large in the town. The whole of Skipton was abuzz with this news. Perhaps a lesser enthusiast of poetry would have been crass enough to suggest all this to Wystan as a subject for his pen. But just as you learn in life never to tell comedians jokes, so I have found it fruitless – and indeed insulting – to offer writers a spur to their imagination. It was

Wordsworth who first pointed out that poetry was emotion recollected in tranquillity. The remark came forcefully to mind in Cambridge once, when I saw Ted Hughes propelled over a weir on the Cam by an ardent but feckless admirer. The punt they were travelling in tipped at an angle of forty degrees or more and the young Hughes sat impassively as a cascade of objects passed him on the way to the bottom of the river. I could see the makings of a Poet Laureate in him there and then. As far as I know he has yet to pluck the event from his store of memory and bring it before us in poetic form. Something to look forward to.

So it was that I understood completely Auden's reticence in wishing to speak of anything serious. I stood peaceably beside the great poet, chatting to him in easy and familiar terms about his poem 'In Praise of Limestone', long a favourite of mine. His craggy and lined features betrayed no special emotion, but at last he interrupted me to explain that he was that day up to his ears in bullocks.

'Bullocks, old lad,' he said, leaning into the auction ring and swishing haphazardly with a wand of hazel. 'So don't talk to me about limestone, sitha, for I'll have none of it.'

I tried him instead on what has always struck me as the strange fascination he seemed to have for the garrison town of Dover. Auden's responses were, I have to say, cagey.

''Tis a funny sort of pub, is that Dover Castle.

D'you know the landlord, d'you? They call him Ray.'

At long length he pressed some money in my hand – coins, warm from his trouser pocket – and bade me go home and write the whole shooting match up, for them as liked that sort of thing. During our colloquy, the rain had become sleet and the sleet snow. It was, as the poet remarked, colder than a witch's tit. For myself, I was on fire with excitement.

'You would encourage me to write, then, Wystan?'

'I would, lad. I've a'ready give thee some brass. Buy youssen a little biro job an' a block of paper. Gerrit it down, all tha moithering. Tha nivver knows. It might save thee from t'nuthouse. Tha can nivver tell. Hasta ivver heared of addled Bert?'

'I have some hundred pages of notes on the man!' I cried, astonished and delighted that a mind as genuinely eclectic as Auden's should have sifted the life of the second Bishop of Prague.

'There y'are, then. Bert wor a religious loonie, but t'old fella wor a dedicated scribbler and it saved his life at the death. Same as might happen to you, happen. You've a sporting chance, put it no higher.'

We shook hands heartily on it. When I left he was downing a cup of Oxo with some market notorieties and planning, as he said, to down a shedful that night. Breath steamed upon the air from raucous laughter. The snow lay round about, deep and crisp and even.

So to my meeting with the solicitors engaged by Mrs Wallfisch. With Auden's incredible encouragements ringing in my head, I was in no mood to banter with them. After some delay, I was ushered into the chambers of Mr Blakeson, senior partner. He was training a cage bird to alight on his finger. We discussed the background to the case: my correspondence with Karl-Otto, our mutual interests, the character of his client and the value of the missing *Denkschrift*. I was strongly reminded of Sandy Powell in talking to the lawyer.

'I have to tell you frankly, Mr Jenks, the late Dr Wallfisch's affairs are in some disarray.'

'I knew no such thing.'

'Well, they are. He was what they call up here an in-comer. Of course, that's all behind us now, the in-comers are good people, we know that. Well, they're not good, they can't be, they know nothing of Yorkshire, but it's water under the bridge is what I'm trying to say. Now Audrey – I know her well, she plays golf at Skipton, did you know I was a golfer, I suppose you can tell – Audrey is wanting to write a book about her hubby. D'you see?'

'If her letter is anything to go by, she would be better off doing something else.'

'Oooh,' Mr Blakeson chided, his Yorkshire sense of the generous outraged for a moment. 'What a sharp tongue. Anyoldhow. She has it in mind to write a little book as I say – and she's given up her Lady Captaincy to do it, so I know it's serious, is this – '

'Mr Blakeson, I will save you the trouble of further ramblings. I do not have the *Denkschrift*. Any more than I have the Maltese Falcon. Your budgerigar has soiled my balaclava. Unless you can come to the point, I shall be forced to make my excuses and leave.'

'Well!' Blakeson muttered. 'I'll go to the foot of our stairs!'

He would have said more, but in the adjoining office there was suddenly the most stupendous scream and together we rushed in, expecting to find the staff at gunpoint.

Instead, there on the carpet, nostrils quivering, one hoof pawing the ground, was the escaped Friesian bull. A 'For Sale' notice decorated its left horn and it was – as they say in the vulgar language of public houses – in a muck sweat. But more, much more: sitting astride it, with a shy yet cheeky schoolboy smile, was W. H. Auden.

'You, you daft beggar!' Mr Blakeson exclaimed.

'How do,' Auden said gaily, doffing his 'Dalesman'.

'Get that animal out of this office! Brenda, phone for the police. When you've done that, ring the RSPCA. Ask for Tiny Thoroughgood, tell him Walter Blakeson wants him, double quick sharp.

Now keep calm everybody. We don't want to go upsetting him. This carpet was only laid last year.'

Auden kicked the animal into a walk and it toured the office, knocking over things at will. Brenda and her colleague Rosemary took refuge on top of a filing cabinet.

'I canna ho'd t'owd lad,' Auden said. 'We've been halfway to Gargave afore he would turn. I wor just mekkin' for't Market Inspector, like, when he belted in here. By, he took them stairs two at a time. Tha don't know him, dosta Mr Blakeson, for he seems to know thee?'

It was my suggestion that we should lead the animal on to the balcony and wait to see what arrangements Mr Thoroughgood of the RSPCA could conjure. The windows leading to the balcony were opened to let in a flurry of snow – and while I pushed from behind, Wystan urged and cajoled the bull out on to the narrow balcony, to the cheers of those within, and those below. Those within were at pains to close the doors behind us, and we hung suspended in the night, forty feet above the main thoroughfare. Below us all was light and movement. The Fire Brigades from Keighley and Ilkley were on hand to assist their colleagues of the Skipton Brigade. Mr Arthur Wainwright, who happened to be passing, paused to make a sketch, and I believe I saw Sir Leonard Hutton in the crowd also, a portion of cod in his calloused but educated hands.

'Fame, old lad,' Auden croaked. 'Greatest day of my life.'

It was the early days of tranquillising darts, and Thoroughgood of the RSPCA, never mind he tipped the scales at twenty stones, was a nervous man. He told me afterwards he had only ever seen them used by Armand and Michaela Denis, and then on black and white television at his mother's house. At all events, his aim was off, and I woke in Skipton General two days later.

Thoroughgood was a good-hearted enough fellow. There was a soft and kindly side to his burly frame and I count him – no matter what happened – one of the better sort of Yorkshiremen. He brought me a bag of Baxter's pork pies, or growlers, as they are known in that part of the world, and ate most of them in absent-minded fashion while describing how they had at last brought down the bull from the balcony using block and tackle. He confided that he hated market day: he had joined the RSPCA because of his interest in tropical fish. As he said, truthfully enough, very few people had ever been hospitalised on account of a koi.

As to Auden, I had several postcards from him before he died. I keep them by me as I revive his memory. On one, showing a reproduced photograph of the Oberkirchen Fire Brigade circa 1900, the poet has indited a row of exclamation marks. Underneath is written this: 'Dearest of nightmares, these are called shriek marks! No more cow stories!'

– *Fourteen* –

My correspondence with the famous has had some curious highways and byways. I think in particular now of an extraordinary tourney of wits I conducted with the late N. I. Khruschev, which began when I mistook this bibulous and argumentative Russian for the inventor of the famous health salts. Nikita and I exchanged waggish postcards for some years after. Another name that I pluck from memory is that of Arthur C. Clarke, to whom I wrote – initially – to enquire whether he was that same Arthur Clarke whom I had misdirected in Dover one spring evening in 1955. He was not. At least, he said he was not. This is a tale worth telling, albeit briefly.

One April evening in Dover I was squeezing out the last pleasures of the day by riding the rocking-horse in a children's playground. I had played a hearty but inconsequential game of tug for my briefcase with some boisterous lads on their way home from the College of Building. I was, as I say, astride the cast-iron saddle when my attention was caught by a man – or youth – walking towards me across the grass. At first blush he was something a little out of the ordinary. Dressed all in silver, he held out huge transparent plastic wings which he sometimes raised to touch above his head. *On* his head was a sort of skin-tight and apertureless balaclava; and where might have been a forelock in Edwardian times was a red eye on the end of a wavering steel stalk. I confess I crouched behind the roundabout for a second or two.

'Hello,' he said. 'Sorry to trouble you, but could you direct me to Walsingham Road?'

This diminished, at any rate in my own mind, the possibility that he had arrived some moments earlier from another planet. I peered at him through the bars of the roundabout.

'You speak very good English,' I temporised, thinking that if he were an alien, or indeed an Angel of the Lord, civility could be well repaid at some point in the not too distant future.

'Oh, do you think so?' the creature said, cheerful but muffled. 'That *is* nice.'

As it happened, I knew full well where to find Walsingham Road and directed the creature by pointing him towards the appropriate quarter of the gathering gloom. His eye nodded.

'Well, I'll be off, then,' he mumbled. 'Thanks for your help. I don't want to be late.'

'Of course not. May I ask your name, and place of origin?'

'Arthur Clarke,' he said. 'From Ramsgate.'

A fancy dress party? Something more sinister? The reader must form his own conclusions here. But the fact of the matter was that I had inadvertently sent the creature to Walsingham Road when he had actually been enquiring for Walnut Tree Road. The poor fellow was made the subject of an outraged citizen's arrest before he could rectify the mistake. 'Colditz Colonel Catches Dover Fairy' ran the next day's headlines.

But that is by the by. How refreshing recently, in turning over the contents of several tea-chests of letters, cards and – occasionally – writs, to come across a correspondence I had with the enchanting Miss Katherine Hepburn, one of Hollywood's own, and a star I am proud to call a dear and honoured friend. There indeed was a woman fit to grace her sex. We met many years ago at Gatwick and the story bears repetition.

Miss Hepburn was at that mighty international airport, I believe, to pay a flying visit to a friend. She walked to the nearest information desk and said simply – in the inimitable way that has so often been imitated – she wished to see Sophia. She meant of course by this Miss Sophia Loren, then married to the distinguished film director, Fred Ponting. A comedy of errors ensued. It was not until she was strapped in, on Bulgarian Airlines Flight JG 441, ready for take-off to Sofia, that the mistake was discovered. There was considerable Balkan merriment. She presented the pilot with an eight-foot chiffon scarf she had been wearing over her hat in a forlorn attempt to be inconspicuous, and left, applauded by the film-loving Bulgars on their way home to their capital city.

As I have indicated, I was also at Gatwick that day. I had for some months past been in correspondence with Mr David Bailey, whom I met quite by chance at a flower show in Kent. The details need not concern us, except to say that I was able to warn the famous photographer seconds before the main exhibition tent was snatched away by storm-force gales. We clung to each other as the tent and several thousand blooms, sprays, dried flower arrangements and vases were lofted over a distant stand of elms. Bailey and I began a correspondence. The good-hearted man at first pretended that he was not the one I had saved from a hurricane in Sidcup – and in a way I liked him all the more for it. I had found him a modest enough man already. But I had his address through his publishers and pressed him hard. I felt confident enough to send him some snapshots I had taken of two swans under a bridge, I forget where, for his comment. He very generously sent me a short critique. He liked my two swans under a bridge but found the focus a little soft. He confessed he had imagined the white bits to be other than swans. The water was very well captured. Was the shoe that set the composition off so tellingly my own? And so forth. He suggested I should expand my range. He would like to see me tackle the model, etc.

For a sophisticate like Bailey (and one with such a beautiful wife) this was easy to propose. It was very much more difficult for me to accomplish. I did not have a compliant woman I could call upon and I was thrown back on large inanimate objects. My study of Didcot Power Station was a bit of a dud: I needed more drama. So it was that I happened to be at Gatwick the day that Miss Hepburn was on the Bulgarian Airlines flight. In fact I was at no time very far away.

Arriving at Gatwick by Rudge posed problems. I was ejected from the short stay car-park by some impudent attendant and pedalled about for a while looking for somewhere to leave the bike. I found my way at last on to the taxi-ing runway and after a few alarms and excursions – what I think are called in the aviation world 'near misses' – managed to chain the faithful Rudge to a spare set of steps. I set off on foot, my Kodak at the ready. I was engaged in a study I ultimately titled 'Wheel and Sky at Gatwick Airport' when the belt of my mackintosh was accidentally engaged with some part of the hydraulic system of the very plane on which Miss Hepburn was sitting, thirty feet above my head. The plane began to move, my belt took a further turn round the wheel and I found myself being towed by the neck at a fast walking pace towards Runway One. (Studying the film when I got it back from Boots, I would say it was about now that I exposed Wheel and Sky.) The situation was becoming serious. A hundred different thoughts flashed through my mind, uppermost being that I had not brought my passport, nor had I any idea to what destination I was taking off. The noise was indescribable.

Then, mercifully, high above my head, the divine Miss Hepburn discovered her mistake, the plane was stopped, and I was spared an uncomfortable and wholly unnecessary journey over southern Europe. Now the plane turned in its tracks and I was once again towed along at a brisk trot, but towards the main buildings. Some steps were brought – with my bicycle chained to them – and I called out to Miss Hepburn as she alighted. She was good enough to point out my predicament to an official, before being whisked away inside.

I reproduce below our subsequent correspondence:

Weymouth, 26 April   Dear Miss Hepburn.
You may remember me as the man entangled in the wheel of an airliner on your visit to Gatwick earlier this year. I should like to thank you for your extreme kindness in mentioning my general situation to the staff. I was sorry not to have had the opportunity to thank you in person, but I was unavoidably

detained for several days, and you had returned to America when I enquired after you in London. Yrs devotedly, etc.

Los Angeles, 17 May   Dear Mr Jenks. Wasn't that a lot of fun? What detained you? You could have bought me a drink. Katherine Hepburn.

Shrewsbury, 29 June   Dear Miss Hepburn. Your very kind letter has been forwarded to me c/o Mrs Walters of 7 Hargreaves Villas, Meole Brace. I was detained at Gatwick by the security police there, charged with attempting to damage a Tupolev Tu-134, and remanded for a psychiatric report. A further charge of air piracy was dropped, upon consideration by the Director of Public Prosecutions. These were small matters compared with my disappointment at not meeting you. Perhaps when you are next in London we might put that to rights? Your performance in *The African Queen* was matched only by our own Dirk Bogarde, who made such a brave stab at the drunken skipper. I saw almost all the film at a showing in February of this year. Many best wishes, etc.

Los Angeles, 12 July   Dirk was magnificent, you are right. I think we were all surprised by the results. Did you know he did that movie entirely without make-up? You say you saw almost all of it. Amaze me: what happened? Love, Kate.

Shrewsbury, 23 July   My dearest Kate. Yr postcard arrived this morning and I hasten to reply. I saw *The African Queen* at Abergavenny and was greatly enjoying it when the front of the cinema was destroyed by a cattle lorry bearing over a hundred sheep to market. The manager very kindly came up on stage and described the outcome of the story as best he could – with feeling, I should hasten to add, but doubtless not so well as the skills employed by Mr Huston. The accident was reported in the local press. Mrs Walters adds her best wishes and thanks you for the colourful bedjacket.

New York, 7 August   Dear Claude. I think I read about the Great Abergavenny Sheep Disaster in *Variety*. That was tough on you all. Huston is in town and I told him all about you. He loved it! Get that goddam bedjacket back from Mrs Walters, you dope. It was a golf cardigan for you. Bestest, Kate.

New York, 13 August   From Mr John Huston. Claude – I am apprised of your determinations in the matter of *Queen*, which was an unusual subject, perfectly rendered as you have said by Kate and Mr Bogarde, an actor for whom I have the highest respect. I am sending you the cap worn by your Mr Bogarde in the picture, as a small embodiment of my sentiment, or if you will, a token of regard from yours truly, John Huston.

Shrewsbury, 3 August   To Mr John Huston. Dear Mr Huston. I am overwhelmed by your kindness. We have a saying in England: if the cap fits, wear it. I thus enclose a photograph of me at the head of the Llanberis Pass, wearing both the cap and a cardigan given to me by Kate Hepburn. The photograph was taken by an obliging Welshman, also a keen cyclist. You will see we had thoroughly Welsh weather of it. It is his Raleigh I am holding in my spare hand. Also find enclosed, as a small and unworthy gift, my 'Wheel and Sky at Gatwick', which I have had enlarged by Peckinpah and Brownlow, of Salop. I have also taken the liberty of preparing a treatment of my book on Adalbert, second Bishop of Prague, and enclose it herein. The full text was rather too heavy to send by air, and follows on by sea-mail. May I thank you once again, Sincerely, etc.

Mexico City, 27 November   From John
Huston. Dear CJ. Your most interesting mail
has been forwarded to me, cognisance of
which has given me opportunity for
approbation. Adalbert I conceive to be one hell
of a fellow – tho' I have yet to read your fuller
text. I was reminded of many things in perusal
of the substantive elements. I know of your
abiding loyalty to British actors: do you think
the young fellow Peter O'Toole a man for the
part? (I notice you describe A. in telling phrase
as a Bohemian to his sandal straps.) I fancy I
descry something altogether very modern in
Adalbert. My good friend Mr Lee Marvin
might do for the Pope; alternatively as the
heathen Prussian who finally does our man in.
You have Adalbert baptising King Stephen: I
wonder if we can move the story on a little and
have him marry him? But these are indeed
peccadilloes. I would like to think about it
some more. I am having your 'Wheel and Sky'
made into my seasonal greetings card for this
year. There's poetry in the damn thing. Yrs
aye. John.

Los Angeles, 20 December   Huston sent me the
picture of you on the Llanberis Pass. From
now on and evermore, you are Johnny Two
Bikes to me. But no more letters, I'm a

working girl. You understand the fragrance of
the moment, no one better. Keep on blowing,
you lonesome whistle. All my love, through
my tears, Katey.

– *Fifteen* –

A night of turmoil! Raising these ghosts has left me *à bout de souffle*, as M. Jean-Luc Godard would have it when he and I were involved in the grand mix-up over sleeper berths on the Newhaven-Dieppe crossing. Perhaps I am coming down with flu. One way or another, I feel myself to be wading through treacle, or, in a vivid metaphor of the Bishop of Durham's, sculpting from frogspawn. Does the public really want the day by day life of Jenks, when he himself can hardly endure the memory of it? I know these mental pangs are a commonplace of autobiography. Though you would hardly suppose so in reading the finished product. How many times do we read such as 'I leaned forward after two thrilling hours and touched her knee. Here I had been talking about myself as the greatest theatrical sensation of the century, in the company of the most beautiful woman in the world. I hastened to put things right and asked Miss Taylor what she thought about me.'

Yesterday while out walking and reflecting, I met the most charming man, a wallpaper salesman from the West Riding of Yorkshire. He was sipping tea and reading from the *Pensées* of Pascal, in the front seat of a car parked neatly in the lay-by near the post office.

'The hardest job in the world, old love,' he said, of the writer's craft. 'This Pascal fella, 'e says here, "Life is a dream, a little more coherent than most." And the lad never saw forty.'

'You're a scholar of Pascal, I take it.'

'No, no, I'm a wallpaper salesman, like I say. But what a time of it 'e 'ad. I mean 'e told the other fellas at the Port Royal – his mates – 'e told them 'e had this big thing he wanted to get off 'is chest. Told them straight up. There's only one of 'em paid a blind bit of notice. 'e pops his clogs, they turn up to the death-bed, like, and find bundles of the stuff. Bundles of it. All scribbled down on bits and pieces, you know. Back of envelope job, most of it. Too late to ask 'im then what 'e was on about.'

I stared at my strange new friend.

'Do you think a book should have short chapters?' I asked.

'I think it should 'ave big print. Are there lasses in your book?'

'Only the very best,' I said in gallantry, mentally omitting Strutt.

'Do you know what I think?' the wallpaper salesman said, wiping the cup of his thermos with an enormous handkerchief. 'I wor in Yarmouth yesterday, thinking about it. This Pascal lad, laid out there like a roll of lino on the bed – it gave me a right queer feeling. All his mates poking around saying what the holy hammer's all this writing job e's left laid about? You know, as though 'e wor a tripe dresser or summat.'

'The matter was at any rate partially resolved by Victor Cousin at the French Academy in 1842.'

'I know,' my salesman friend chuckled. 'But that did nowt for our kid, like. He'd been pushing up the daisies for – what wor it – hundred and eighty years. Hardest job in the world, like I say.'

Or did I dream all this? I woke this morning at all events with but one name on my lips.

Come, trusty Underwood. Lend my words wings.

– *Sixteen* –

'The trouble with you, Jenks, is that being has totally replaced doing. Your life has become your full-time occupation.'

Thus the greatest Englishman it has ever been my pleasure to meet.

'I fancy some of the great philosophies the world has known would gently commend that state of affairs.'

'Indeed they would,' came the gruff reply. 'And I was speaking not a little out of envy.'

My interlocutor was none other than Sir Harold Macmillan. He was then in the sere and yellow leaf. We met quite by chance one rain-soaked morning at Cromer, that most pleasant of seaside towns. It would be true to say I bumped into him, for that is exactly what happened. The grand old statesman was descending backwards from a pensioners' excursion coach as I was being impelled down the promenade by a force nine gale, blowing all the way from Siberia. The month was, as I recall, June. Some minutes earlier the Cromer lifeboat had been launched.

Macmillan – I should better call him Lord Stockton, for by then that is what he was – was wearing his famous cardigan, topped by an ankle-length transparent mackintosh and the hat given to him by Nikita Khruschev. I soon had him disentangled from the spokes of the Rudge and up on his feet again. Bending to the wind, we made our way to a nearby hotel, in order to take shelter from flying deckchairs. I ordered tea.

'I should, I know, call you Lord Stockton, my lord, but somehow your earlier titles are more familiar to my tongue.'

'Everybody calls me Uncle Harold these days,' the old man smiled, showing me at once the dry humour for which he will always be remembered. 'And you, what may I call you?'

'My name is Claude Jenks.'

'Mr Jenks, sit on my good side if you will and amuse me. There has been bingo arranged for us all in some other part of town, but this is more to my taste.'

What did we not talk about that day? Sulphur-yellow seas crashed over the promenade and the pier shook to its foundations: Macmillan and I sat entranced in each other's company. For my part, I was luxuriating in an older order of England, one that this great man so ably represented, both here and round the world.

'But you,' he objected gently, 'have the greater story to tell.'

'You knew both Stalin and Kennedy.'

'Yet *you* knew Doris Day.'

'Our acquaintance was slight.'

'Such beautiful teeth,' Macmillan murmured wistfully. 'And I don't know that Miss Day would not have been a better companion at dinner than Stalin. Though why you should think I ever met old Joe, I can't for the life of me imagine. I knew Kennedy. He was in Accounts. You seem to have met a very great number of the famous, Mr Jenks.'

'Let us say our paths have crossed.'

'Most propitiously, by your account of it.'

He had made a simple ballista by balancing his coffee spoon across the handle of an overturned fork; and now – banging with his mottled hand upon the end of the spoon – he sent a cube of sugar across the room. It rattled against the wainscotting.

'Dear old Nanny,' he muttered absently. 'Tell me, Jenks. Do you ever have the feeling that the best is over?'

I hesitated. Macmillan patted my hand.

'I see that you do. Yet from this one sentiment, dear friend, Europe has fashioned and refashioned its civilisation. No irony could be more sublime. We are on the ship of fools, looking about us in despair. The only horizon we can find is the one that leads us back into the past, whence we came. And our instinct is a good one, by and large. Like oarsmen, we navigate with our backs to the future.'

I was writing this down on a napkin as fast as he was saying it. The great old statesman stayed me with a melancholy smile that peeped from either side of his moustache.

'Let me put it another way. I sense you are a man made indignant by the tone and accent of the present.'

'I am not a very now person,' I admitted.

'No, you are not,' Macmillan agreed. 'I saw that about you the moment you knocked me over in the street out there. Order two large brandies, my dear man, and tell me of your greatest moment, in quartering this island on that mighty Rudge of yours. Though,' he added with a twinkle, 'I believe I may guess what that was.'

He lifted his hand in that affected weariness so endearing to his public, and the room waiter came running. We settled back like characters in a Conrad story.

One of the more intriguing of the family *Ericaceae* is *Monotropa Hypopitys*, the common name for which is Yellow Bird's Nest. It occurs in woods of pine and beech and flowers, as we all know, in summer. My attention was drawn to this modest denizen of our shadier locations by a Mr Tebbitt, of

Chingford. Though it forms no part of my tale, I should add most emphatically that my Mr Tebbitt is no relation to the distinguished broadcaster and political philosopher, Norman Tebbitt. The man I met was of a very different cast, or mould. Dressed in a shapeless grey suit, his blue chin sporting razor nicks, his eyes as dark-ringed as a panda's, the Tebbitt I knew was clinging to sanity by the tips of his fingers. I was unfortunate enough to sit next to him for a few minutes on a bench by the Embankment. His interest in botany was as a source of metaphor for our present woes, and though I do not understand it, I reproduce the thrust of his principal point.

'The roots, do you see? It's all in the roots,' Tebbitt grated in his corncrake voice. 'Yellow Bird's Nest, the roots resting in decayed matter. Do you follow me so far?'

'Indeed. To the letter. You can if you wish let go of my lapels.'

'But,' Tebbitt whispered theatrically, ignoring my request and tightening his madman's grip upon my coat, 'if you look at those roots carefully, you see them coated with a fine web of gunk – and do you know what that gunk is? I'll tell you. The roots are covered with *Mycorrhiza*, a fungus. It's the fungus that does the work for the plant, and without the fungus, the root is useless. That is my point.'

'And exceedingly well taken. But what exactly

has that to do with what I took to be your actual subject, the role of the BBC in the affairs of the nation at the present time?'

'I'll tell you,' Tebbitt said, and would have begun the whole sorry rigmarole again, but for the approach of men with white coats who advanced towards us at a brisk trot.

However, he had sowed a seed of interest – not in the plight of the BBC, that strange congerie of accountants and press officers – but in our old friend the Yellow Bird's Nest. I was about to undertake a visit to Lincoln, for some other purpose, and determined to step a little out of my way to visit the site where last I had chanced on the scruffy little saprophyte.

'And here,' I said to Macmillan, 'I come to the bones of my yarn. Would you like to guess where that was?'

He drew on a panatella for a moment, and examined the glowing tip with appreciation.

'My instinct inclines me to look in this very county,' he murmured.

'*Exactement*!'

A week or so after meeting with the unfortunate Tebbitt, I was on my hands and knees in pine needles, deep within the woods at Sandringham, face to face with *Monotropa Hypopitys* and its friend the fungus. There was a footfall, or to be more exact, four footfalls – and there peering inquisitively at me round the pale-yellow scales of the plant was a sharp-nosed face, inches from my own. As I drew back to get things in better focus, I perforce let out an involuntary gasp. Yes! A sharp nose, dark eyes, ears erect – I was looking into the face of a corgi!

'Great heavens! And I suppose you still had on your bicycle clips and so forth?'

'Bicycle clips, working mittens and a black plastic sou'wester. I jumped to my feet and faced – ' I hesitated ' – she who I would prefer to call the Lady with the Corgi.'

'Your tact is exemplary,' the old Prime Minister murmured. 'And what did Her Maj – the Lady – what did she have to say? I know you will have total recall.'

He was of course right: I remembered every last detail of that wonderful moment.

'What are you doing here in my wood?' she began as I tore at the elastic to my sou'wester the better to doff it.

'I was examining *Mycorrhiza*, Ma'am.'

'And must you do that here? Couldn't you examine your Corrhiza somewhere else?'

'And *Monotropa Hypopitys*.'

'*Votr' otropa? Mais, quelle blague, m'sieur*,' she replied in instant salty French.

'No, Ma'am, you fail to understand – '

The Lady with the Corgi narrowed her eyes.

'I what?' she asked.

'I am your humble subject Claude Jenks, amateur botanist, cyclist and scholar.'

'Well, Mr Jenks, you are trespassing on my property. Is that a bomb in your gas-mask case?'

'A thermos of tea, Ma'am.'

'Is there any in it?'

'Indeed.'

'Enough for two?'

So it was that the Lady and I sat down on a carpet of pine needles and shared a flask of Orange Pekoe. Though I may not be believed, she also was gracious enough to accept a macaroon. Thanks to her innate kindliness, I found myself completely at ease, not to say voluble. The little cake stayed half eaten in her dainty fingers. I had her full attention.

'And tell me,' she asked. 'One sees so little from cars. Is the old half-timbered café still standing on the A 34, just before you turn off for Tamworth? Can you still get those wonderful tea-towels in Stoke Poges? And that appalling factory one sees between Leamington and Coventry – what is made there?'

'I believe that is the University of Warwick, Ma'am,' I muttered apologetically.

The Lady with the Corgi shook her head in wonder.

'You don't say. Here is a puzzler for you, Jenks: can one still buy cloth at Dewsbury Market on a Wednesday? That second-hand bookshop in Crich – have they done anything about the stair carpet? Does the Hornblower still blow curfew at Ripon?

And what about the Crab Man of Hunstanton –
what news of him?'

Macmillan reached for his brandy with a shaking
hand. Tears ran like silent rivers down his papery
cheeks. I myself was blubbing like a child.

'In short, my friend, you found a treasure in the
woods.'

'I did indeed.'

'Dry your eyes, you stout fellow. Let that conversation be your justification, root and essence of your
restless life. No man could seek higher.'

Together we stood to attention and saluted the
wall and a hotplate of business lunches. Macmillan
turned and shook me by the hand.

'I shall dream of you, Mr Jenks. Have no doubt
of that. And I believe in doing so, I shall join others
who have done the same. And now, if the wind has
abated even a little, take my arm like a good chap
and walk me to the end of the pier. There is much I
would like to reflect upon.'

And so we battled, the grand old man and I,
across the road to the thrumming boardwalks of the
pier. At Macmillan's request, I tied him to the rails
with the belt of my mackintosh, and there we clung,
each of us gazing out to sea with our thoughts and
memories, until brought in by a team of police and
traffic wardens.

– *Seventeen* –

For the time being at least, the blizzard of creativity has run its course. Last night, when I was typing up a letter to the local council, it matters not upon what subject, the exclamation mark key of the faithful old Underwood flew off and hit me a painful blow in the eye. In making an involuntary leap backwards, I fell against the bookshelves and once again they came tumbling down, bringing with them the remains of the plaster. As a sympathetic Strutt has shrewdly observed, it has all ended in tears, just as she said it would. I am continuing these last pages in pencil and with a moist teabag taped over the affected eye. This is a sovereign remedy of Mrs Strutt's, more efficacious than cucumber, in her opinion.

I have left much untold. My brush with Mr James Last at the Horse of the Year Show; an evening spent in the company of Melvyn Bragg and

Miss Anita Brookner at Rhyll; how I came to join the training camp of Muhammed Ali in his title fight with Henry Cooper, and much else besides. The great controversies of my life: Jenks v. The Royal Shakespeare Company; Jenks v. Chester Zoo and parties – these and the real story of my work on Adalbert, Bishop of Prague, a tale of heartbreak and adversity if ever there was one, must wait another day. Faced with an ultimatum from Strutt, I have packed up the major part of my book collection and entrusted it to the loft – fourteen tea-chests of indispensable companions, whom it might be said I am leaving in the lurch.

'I thought you were leaving them in the loft, dear,' old Strutt murmured, her hands round the Brown Betty in her own accommodation. Television blathered in a corner. Some bearded man in a woman's sweater was conducting an interview with a young woman whose chest appeared to have been prepared for open-heart surgery. Mrs Strutt's parakeet perched despondently on the toaster.

'Do you know,' I asked, 'I was once the world's greatest expert on early Bohemia – at any rate in English? Does that matter to you, Mrs Strutt?'

'Don't spit,' the landlady said. 'I know you to be a blinding brainbox of a human being, of course I do. But yours are the ways of the wanderer, my old darling. The settled occupation of my attic for the last fourteen months has done you no good at all. You've hardly had old Roger Rudge out for a spin since spring.'

'You see me as a sadhu, do you?'

'You were born sad, sweetheart. My Frank was just the same.'

'A man seldom spoken of in this house.'

'Also born under a wandering star.'

It is true the Rudge has hardly come out of the coal-shed in all these many weeks. I have been pulled down by mediocrity and varicose veins. But once my mind is made up, I am as remorseless as the tiger. And my mind is made up to take to the road again, no matter what I shall find. Yeats it was who pointed out you could have a good life, or good art. I prefer a good stint at the pedals to either.

Laugh at Jenks if you will, but there'll always be an England. I have the agreement of the Duchess of Devonshire here, who replied to a letter of mine that insofar as she could understand me, I enjoyed cycling in Derbyshire and elsewhere, and to this extent she gave me her unqualified support. In my letter, I hope I implied more. All of us who are truly English can feel it, this hunger to return our great land to a better sort of future. I do not want my beloved country left to the government of those who in previous generations would have populated the pages of detective fiction as minor and often comically dull characters. Let them go away, these grocers and accountants. They have done us damage enough.

I sometimes feel it is only a matter of time before the Foreign Secretary, for example, is called Gary. For myself, I would rather pedal down what country lanes we have left with naught but the cry of the curlew for companion. A plague on the modern. The Hereditary Earl Marshal of England and I once played clock golf at Hunstanton. His Grace commended both my putting stroke and my plea for a return to more civilised values. He too remembered the old threepenny bit with affection. He too believed the nation a better place when the knees of women were an object of romantic mystery.

The Parish Church of St Oswald in Steep Malling is named for that Oswald who was made Bishop of Worcester about 959 and became Archbishop of York fifteen years later. He was a great encourager of learning and learned men. I have specially fond thoughts of that good old man as a consequence. St Dunstan required him to hold the two sees, of Worcester and York, and so we may picture Oswald pretty much on the road for most of his latter years. He died in Worcester on 29 February 992, and even then he was not done with travelling, for ten years later his body was dug up and taken north. When saddle-tramping with the Rudge, I often think of him going about an England packed with wolves, its forest paths strewn with spent arrows and discarded pieces of saddlery. My heart goes out to him, the old psalm-singer. Today he would not be able to ride more than a mile or so before coming across a fast food concession.

On a particular balmy day in 1960 I was in Steep Malling looking for flints. I made my way across tussocky meadows to the squat tower of St Oswald's, peeping over the tops of ancient oaks. As I approached, I heard a man singing the 'Blaydon Races' in a high clear alto. That man was John Betjeman. He was sitting in a wheelbarrow in the church environs, his famous old hat filled with blackberries. I came close and introduced myself.

'Jenks,' Betjeman said, 'you have no need of introduction, if you are that same Jenks that corresponded with my dear chum Malcolm Muggeridge about sin. Are you he? In any case, have a blackberry.'

'I did have something to say to Mr Muggeridge on the point,' I allowed, dipping into the proffered trilby.

'Good. He hasn't the faintest idea what it is, save that it exists in others. I knew we should meet one day. I am very pleased to see you. Take my arm, like a good chap, and let us walk by the river for a while.'

And this we did, though Betjeman insisted we bring the sexton's wheelbarrow, for the pleasure the

noise its squeaking wheel afforded. The poet sauntered beside me, his arm through mine.

'They don't fully understand us, Jenks. I expect
you've noticed. To know something, however small,
about the weeds in this hedgerow, to take pleasure
in rooks, to go from that to *Lalla Rookh*, and on
again to *Corvus Corax* and poor Edgar Allan. Did
you know he rose to the rank of sergeant-major
while writing two collections of poetry? Something
of a first, I would say. *You* understand me in all
this, but how many others? Is the wheelbarrow
heavy, dear heart? Tip the gravestone out if it is.'

We sat on the grass and somehow or other the
talk turned to bicycles.

'You mean you don't have one?'

'I've been thinking about purchasing one.'

'You must! You absolutely must. And it must be
a Rudge, with the c-section mudguards. Get the
biggest frame you can, and have the wheels shod
with Michelin RoadMasters. A bell is rather a poor
thing these days. There used to be one with an
external striker but I think you should look for the
older kind of horn. For heaven's sake don't buy one
of those tin things.'

'Where should I look?'

'My dear fellow. One buys a bike at Oxford. I'll
give you John Sparrow's address. Tell me what
you've been up to today – gossip with me.'

'I have been looking for flints, John.'

'And did you find any?'

'Not as such.'

'Then,' he said, with a radiant smile, 'how lucky you are, for you have fired a small arrow of desire into tomorrow. How I envy you. You are looking a bit moist in the eye, O Claude.'

'I am tremendously touched by what you said about luck.'

'Oh yes,' Betjeman said negligently. 'Luck is the postponement of disappointment. We shall never suffer *that*. Right. Pooh-sticks or leap-frog? You choose.'

'Leap-frog.'

He made a back for me and I ran joyously towards him.